Word Games
2–3

Written by
Linda Schwartz

Editor: Carla Hamaguchi
Illustrator: Darcy Tom
Designer/Production: Moonhee Pak/Cari Helstrom
Cover Designer: Barbara Peterson
Art Director: Tom Cochrane
Project Director: Carolea Williams

Table of Contents

Vocabulary Fun

Riddle Time

Analogies

Fun with Words

Introduction

Each book in the *Power Practice*™ series contains dozens of ready-to-use activity pages to provide students with skill practice. Use the fun activities to supplement and enhance what you are already teaching in your classroom. Give an activity page to students as independent class work, or send the pages home as home-work to reinforce skills taught in class. An answer key is provided for quick reference.

Word Games 2–3 is filled with challenging puzzles and word games to help students improve their vocabulary and spelling as well as sharpen their creative thinking skills. The book is divided into nine main sections:

- **Picture Puzzles**
  Students color pictures and review phonics, consonant blends, digraphs, syllables, rhyming words, and more.

- **Word Scramble**
  Students unscramble words that help reinforce and review short and long vowel sounds as well as consonant blends.

- **Word Search Puzzles**
  These word search puzzles are correlated to science and social studies topics as well as holidays. Students find and circle the 15 hidden words going across and down.

- **Category Games**
  Students list words beginning with specific letters of the alphabet for five categories. They are encouraged to use reference materials to find unusual answers. Students earn points for correct answers. Invite them to exchange game sheets and easily check answers.

- **Crossword Puzzles**
  These puzzles range from easy to more difficult and include crossword puzzles for rhyming, parts of speech, synonyms, antonyms, homophones, plurals, and more.

- **Vocabulary Fun**
  These fun puzzle sheets are designed to challenge students to use a dictionary to look up unusual words and write them under the proper headings. Topics are correlated to language, science, math, and social studies.

- **Riddle Time**
  Students solve riddles by crossing words off a chart and, at the same time, they review parts of speech, phonics, synonyms, and more.

- **Analogies**
  Students solve analogies that relate to synonyms, antonyms, homophones, rhyming words, parts to whole, characteristics, and more. Great practice for standardized tests and critical thinking.

- **Fun with Words**
  This is a collection of fantastic puzzles, including Three-Letter Opposites, Odd Word Out, Compound Match-Ups, and Magic Word Squares.

Use these ready-to-go activities to "recharge" skill review and give students the power to succeed!

Name _____ Date _____

Consonant Blend Clown

Phonics, Spelling, and Writing

Write the correct consonant blend for each word in the clown.

dr	tr	wh	bl	cr	cl

Follow these directions to color the clown:

1. Color all the shapes with the **dr** blend red.
2. Color all the shapes with the **tr** blend blue.
3. Color all the shapes with the **wh** blend orange.
4. Color all the shapes with the **bl** blend yellow.
5. Color all the shapes with the **cr** blend purple.
6. Color all the shapes with the **cl** blend brown.

_____ast

_____ate

_____ail

_____ale

_____imb

_____arf

_____iz

_____en

_____ift

_____ine

_____ag

_____ich

_____anket

Give your clown a name. On the back of your paper, write a story about your clown.

Word Games • 2–3 © 2005 Creative Teaching Press

Phonics Fish

Phonics, Spelling, and Writing

Write the correct consonant blend for each word in the fish.

st	sn	gr	sk	fr	br

Follow these directions to color the fish:

1. Color all the shapes with the **st** blend red.
2. Color all the shapes with the **sn** blend blue.
3. Color all the shapes with the **gr** blend orange.
4. Color all the shapes with the **sk** blend yellow.
5. Color all the shapes with the **fr** blend purple.
6. Color all the shapes with the **br** blend brown.

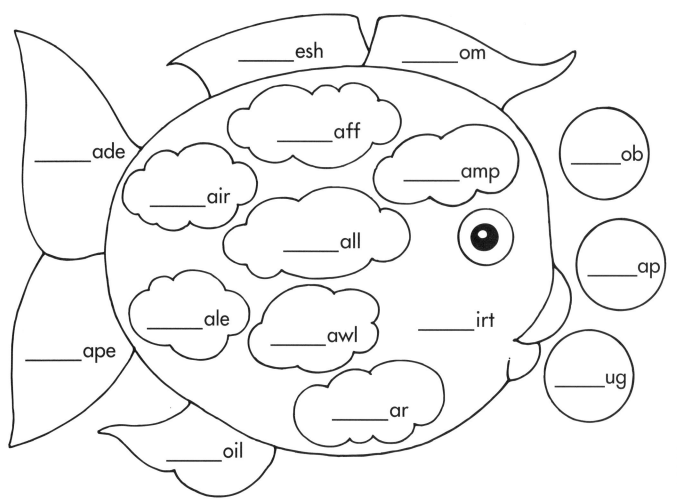

On the back of your paper, write a short story about an adventure this fish has.

Word Games • 2–3 © 2005 Creative Teaching Press

Consonant Digraph Flower

Phonics, Spelling, and Writing

Write the correct consonant digraph at the beginning of each word in the picture.

kn	ch	ph	wr	th

Follow these directions to color the flower and butterfly:

1. Color all the shapes with the **kn** digraph orange.
2. Color all the shapes with the **ch** digraph green.
3. Color all the shapes with the **ph** digraph brown.
4. Color all the shapes with the **wr** digraph yellow.
5. Color all the shapes with the **th** digraph red.

_____em

_____ank

_____oto

_____is

_____e

_____ack

_____it

_____estle

_____ife

_____ight

_____ead

_____eer

_____one

_____op

_____ill

On the back of your paper, write a short story about a butterfly.

Bubble Gum Digraphs

Phonics, Spelling, and Writing

Write the correct consonant digraph that ends each word in the bubble gum machine.

ch	ck	ng	th

Follow these directions to color the picture:

1. Color all the shapes with the **ch** digraph yellow.
2. Color all the shapes with the **ck** digraph green.
3. Color all the shapes with the **ng** digraph blue.
4. Color all the shapes with the **th** digraph orange.
5. Color the bottom part of the bubble gum machine red.

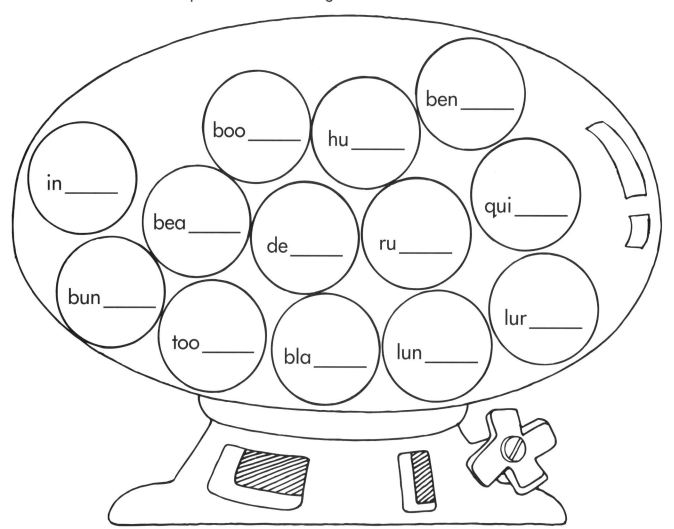

On the back of your paper, write a funny story about a piece of bubble gum.

Who's Wise?

Phonics, Spelling, and Writing

If the consonant *c* has the soft sound of /s/ in a word (as in **city**), color the shape brown.
If the consonant *c* has the hard sound of /k/ in a word (as in **cut**), color the shape orange.
Color the leaves green and the branches yellow.

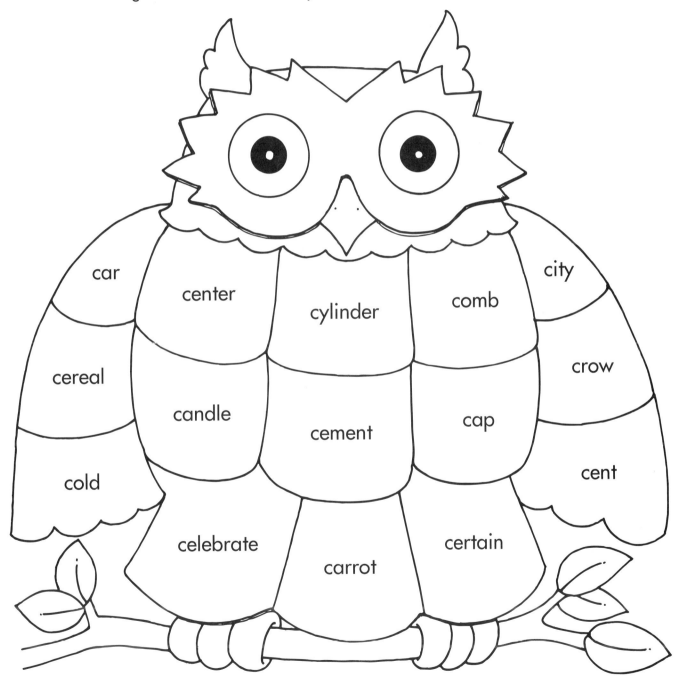

On the back of your paper, write a short story about a wise owl and a lesson he or she teaches someone.

Going for Gold

Phonics, Spelling, and Writing

If the consonant *g* has the soft sound of /j/ in a word (as in **gem**), color the coin yellow.
If the consonant *g* has the hard sound of /g/ in a word (as in **grew**), color the coin orange.
Add drawings and designs to the outside
of the treasure chest and color it.

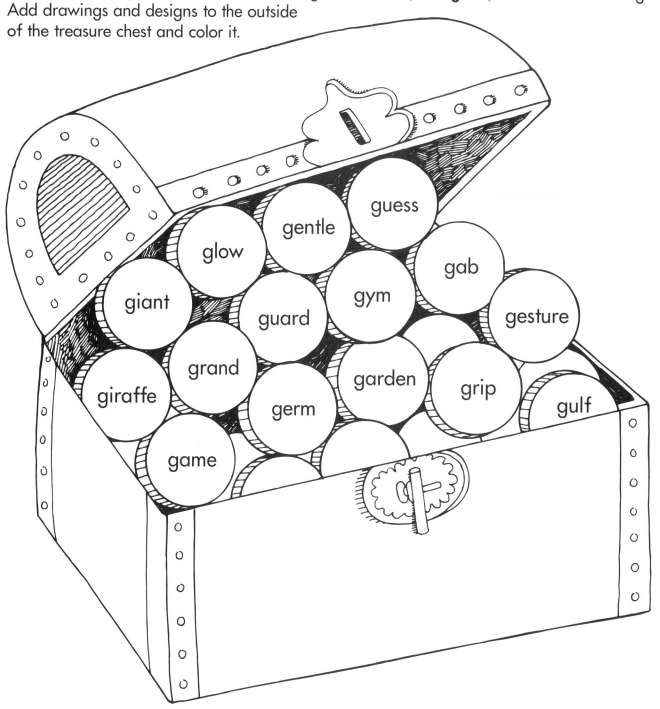

On the back of your paper, draw a treasure map to show where this chest is hidden, or write a story about a lost treasure chest full of gold coins.

Word Games • 2–3 © 2005 Creative Teaching Press

Name _____ Date _____

Syllable Seal

Phonics, Spelling, and Writing

Use this code to color the balls:

1-syllable words = red   3-syllable words = blue   5-syllable words = yellow
2-syllable words = orange   4-syllable words = green   6-syllable words = purple

Give the seal a name. On the back of your paper, write a story about an interesting day he or she has at the zoo.

Word Games • 2–3 © 2005 Creative Teaching Press

Double Scoops

Phonics, Spelling, and Writing

Fill in the missing double consonants in each word. Then use the code to color the ice-cream scoops.

bb	dd	ff	ll	rr	tt

bb = pink   **ff** = green   **rr** = orange
dd = yellow   **ll** = brown   **tt** = red

bo____le

ga____ey

si____y

co____ee

e____or

hi____ing

ra____it

mi____le

hi____y

flu____y

ru____ish

mu____y

ca____age

so____y

li____le

te____or

On the back of your paper, write two or more words for each double consonant.

Name _____ Date _____

Rhyming Word Robot

Phonics, Spelling, and Writing

Use this code to color the robot:

rhymes with **bake** = red   rhymes with **best** = brown   rhymes with **bay** = purple
rhymes with **beat** = yellow rhymes with **bright** = orange rhymes with **bit** = black
rhymes with **bring** = green rhymes with **blot** = blue

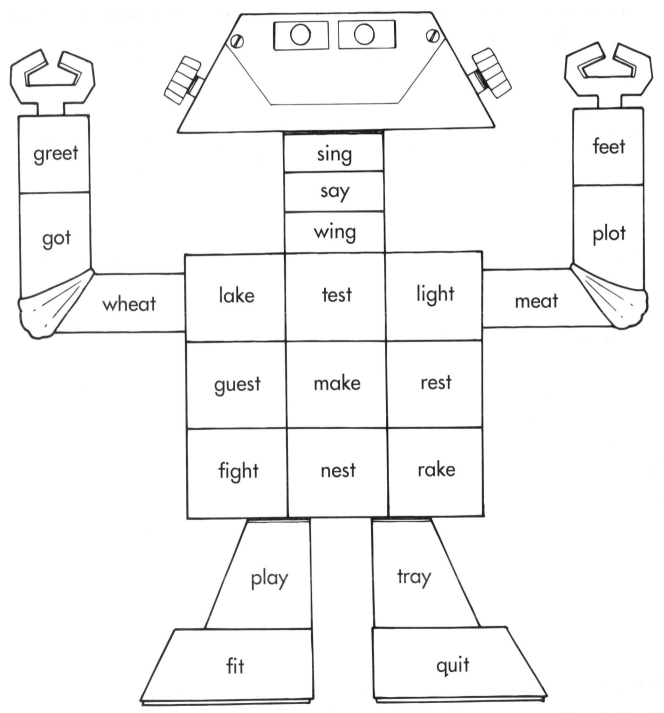

Word Games • 2–3 © 2005 Creative Teaching Press

Name _____ Date _____

Colorful Words

Phonics, Spelling, and Vocabulary

Unscramble the letters in each crayon to spell a word with the short **a** sound. Write the words on the lines. Use the words in the box if you need help.

back	camp	fan	plan	sat	van
cap	had	mat	sand	tack	tag

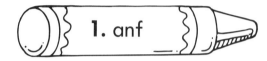 **1.** anf

_____

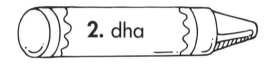 **2.** dha

_____

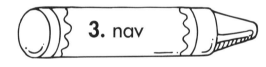 **3.** nav

_____

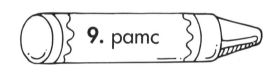 **4.** atm

_____

 **5.** tas

_____

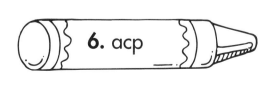 **6.** acp

_____

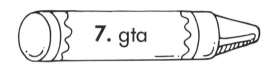 **7.** gta

_____

 **8.** cakb

_____

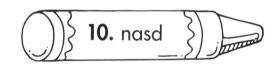 **9.** pamc

_____

10. nasd

_____

11. tcak

_____

12. nalp

_____

Word Games • 2–3 © 2005 Creative Teaching Press

Scrambled Eggs

Phonics, Spelling, and Vocabulary

Unscramble the letters in each egg to spell a word with the short **e** sound. Write the words on the lines. Use the words in the box if you need help.

beg	best	fed	kept	rest	west
bell	desk	jet	men	web	wet

1. tew

_____

2. def

_____

3. jte

_____

4. mne

_____

5. egb

_____

6. bwe

_____

7. steb

_____

8. lebl

_____

9. sked

_____

10. stre

_____

11. wtse

_____

12. kpet

_____

Word Games • 2–3 © 2005 Creative Teaching Press

What's the Scoop?

Phonics, Spelling, and Vocabulary

Unscramble the letters in each ice-cream scoop to spell a word with the short **i** sound. Write the words on the lines. Use the words in the box if you need help.

big	did	fix	hint	pick	wig
bit	fill	him	milk	pin	win

1. xfi

_____

2. tib

_____

3. igb

_____

4. ddi

_____

5. mhi

_____

6. igw

_____

7. niw

_____

8. lilf

_____

9. npi

_____

10. mlik

_____

11. cpik

_____

12. inht

_____

Alphabet Soup

Phonics, Spelling, and Vocabulary

Unscramble the letters in the bowl of soup to spell words with the short **o** sound. Write the words on the lines. Use the words in the box if you need help.

box	hot	hop	lot	mop	rock
fog	fox	job	mom	pop	sock

1. oph

_____

2. pmo

_____

3. ofg

_____

4. bxo

_____

5. toh

_____

6. olt

_____

7. ppo

_____

8. boj

_____

9. oxf

_____

10. mmo

_____

11. rcok

_____

12. sokc

_____

Name _____ Date _____

The Jelly Bean Jar

Phonics, Spelling, and Vocabulary

Unscramble the letters in each jelly bean to spell words with the short **u** sound. Write the words on the lines. Use the words in the box if you need help.

bug	cub	duck	hug	must	rub
bump	cup	dug	fun	pup	rug

1. cbu

5. ppu

9. sumt

_____

2. unf

6. bur

10. pumb

_____

3. gur

7. puc

11. udkc

_____

4. hgu

8. udg

12. ugb

_____

Word Games • 2–3 © 2005 Creative Teaching Press

Hooray for Long A

Phonics, Spelling, and Vocabulary

Unscramble the letters to spell words with the long **a** sound that match the pictures. Write the words on the lines.

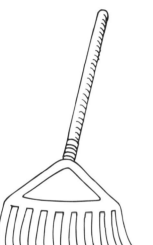

1 ckae _____

2 nace _____

3 akle _____

4 faec _____

5 kare _____

6 veac _____

7 rian _____

8 snaek _____

9 eihtg _____

10 fraem _____

Long E, Please

Phonics, Spelling, and Vocabulary

Unscramble the letters to spell words with the long **e** sound that match the pictures. Write the words on the lines.

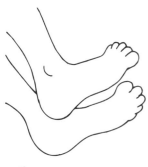

1 ebe _____

2 yek _____

3 eta _____

4 laef _____

5 teeb _____

6 tsea _____

7 tefe _____

8 erte _____

9 mtae _____

10 wahet _____

Word Games • 2–3 © 2005 Creative Teaching Press

I Like Long I

Phonics, Spelling, and Vocabulary

Unscramble the letters to spell words with the long **i** sound that match the pictures.
Write the words on the lines.

1 pei _____

2 ciem _____

3 mide _____

4 bkie _____

5 vife _____

6 keit _____

7 neni _____

8 tmei _____

9 nigth _____

10 simel _____

Name _____ Date _____

I Know Long O
Phonics, Spelling, and Vocabulary

Unscramble the letters to spell words with the long **o** sound that match the pictures. Write the words on the lines.

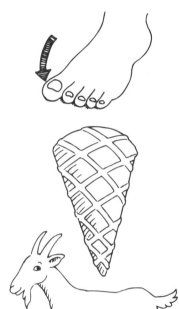

1 teo _____

2 daor _____

3 soer _____

4 hsoe _____

5 nobe _____

6 saop _____

7 cneo _____

8 neso _____

9 toag _____

10 glbeo _____

Word Games • 2–3 © 2005 Creative Teaching Press

Name _____ Date _____

Cute Long U

Phonics, Spelling, and Vocabulary

Unscramble the letters to spell words with the long **u** sound. Write the words on the lines.
Use the words in the box if you need help.

blue	bugle	cube	flute	huge
rude	tube	tune	unit	use

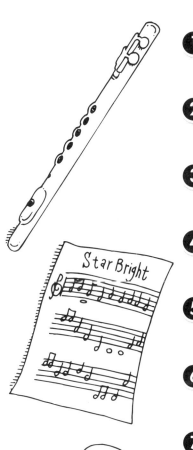

1 seu _____

2 lueb _____

3 cbeu _____

4 ehgu _____

5 nuti _____

6 tuen _____

7 ured _____

8 bute _____

9 buleg _____

10 leftu _____

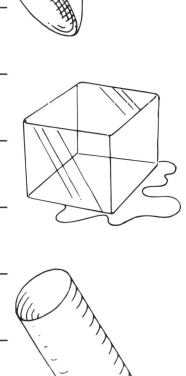

Word Scramble

Phonics, Spelling, and Vocabulary

Unscramble the letters to spell words that match the pictures. Write the words on the lines.

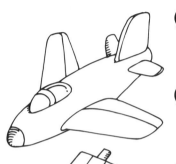

1 crbi _____

2 slde _____

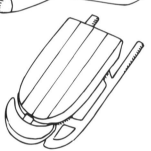

3 crba _____

4 plnea _____

5 clkco _____

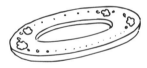

6 pltae _____

7 frtiu _____

8 skkun _____

9 spono _____

10 whela _____

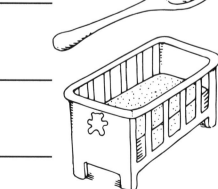

Name _____ Date _____

Bird Search

Science, Spelling, and Vocabulary

Find and circle the names of the birds hidden in the puzzle. Words can be found going from left to right and top to bottom.

bluebird	flamingo	penguin	cardinal	hawk
raven	dove	ostrich	robin	duck
owl	swan	eagle	pelican	woodpecker

```
W R O B I N D E G
O S T R I C H A N
O F L A M I N G O
D U C K P S W A N
P B L U E B I R D
E E A G L E H L R
C A R D I N A L A
K O E O C O W L V
E W D V A O K L E
R I P E N G U I N
```

Word Games • 2–3 © 2005 Creative Teaching Press

Color Search

Science, Spelling, and Vocabulary

Find and circle the names of the colors hidden in the puzzle. Words can be found going from left to right and top to bottom.

black	green	red	blue	navy
silver	brown	orange	tan	gold
pink	white	gray	purple	yellow

```
G  R  E  E  N  A  V  Y     N
R  R  T  A  B  G  R  A  Y
W  L  S  R  L  O  P  R  G
H  Y  I  T  B  L  U  E  P
I  E  L  A  R  D  R  D  I
T  L  V  N  O  B  P  E  N
E  L  E  D  W  N  L  H  K
U  O  R  A  N  G  E  B  I
H  W  B  L  A  C  K  D  E
```

Word Games • 2–3 © 2005 Creative Teaching Press

Name _____ Date _____

Mammal Search

Science, Spelling, and Vocabulary

Find and circle the names of the mammals hidden in the puzzle. Words can be found going from left to right and top to bottom.

bear	fox	leopard	beaver	giraffe
lion	deer	goat	sheep	donkey
horse	tiger	elephant	kangaroo	zebra

```
N E D O N K E Y L
E Z G I R A F F E
A S R R T N G L O
Z H B P I G O I P
E E E I G A A O A
B E A V E R T N R
R P R E R O D Y D
A F O X H O R S E
N O A V T X F E E
E L E P H A N T R
```

Name _____ Date _____

Flower Search

Science, Spelling, and Vocabulary

Find and circle the names of the flowers hidden in the puzzle. Words can be found going from left to right and top to bottom.

daffodil	jasmine	petunia	daisy	lilac
rose	gardenia	marigold	sunflower	hibiscus
orchid	tulip	iris	pansy	violet

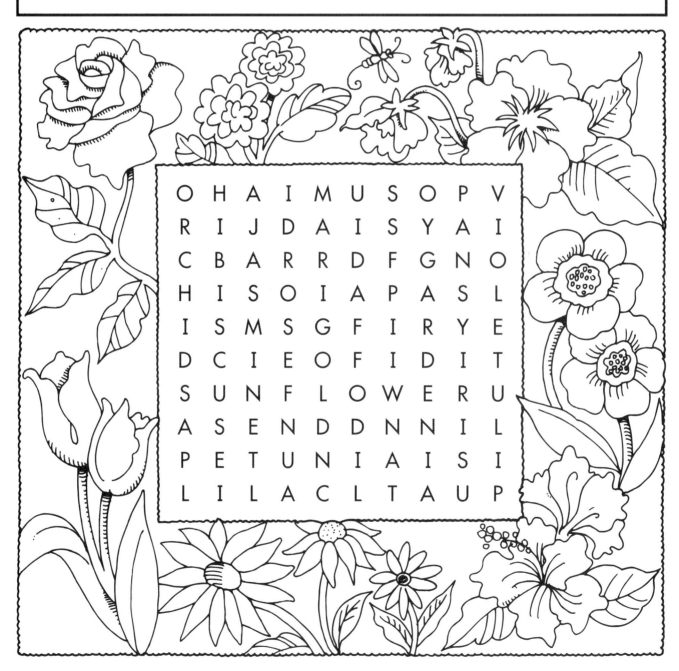

Word Games • 2–3 © 2005 Creative Teaching Press

Name _____ Date _____

Fruit Search

Science, Spelling, and Vocabulary

Find and circle the names of the fruits hidden in the puzzle. Words can be found going from left to right and top to bottom.

apple	grapefruit	pear	banana	kiwi
pineapple	blackberry	lemon	raspberry	blueberry
lime	strawberry	grape	orange	watermelon

```
R O R A N G E S G B K
A P R A A E C T R L I
S L P P E A R R A U W
P G N I E G R A P E I
B B A N A N A W E B R
E O L E M O N B F E L
R B L A C K B E R R Y
R A P P L E E R U R P
Y P N P G E E R I Y R
P R E L I M E Y T E A
W A T E R M E L O N C
```

Word Games • 2–3 © 2005 Creative Teaching Press

Vegetable Search

Science, Spelling, and Vocabulary

Find and circle the names of the vegetables hidden in the puzzle. Words can be found going from left to right and top to bottom.

asparagus	cabbage	okra	beans	carrot
onion	beet	cauliflower	peas	broccoli
celery	potato	brussels sprouts	corn	squash

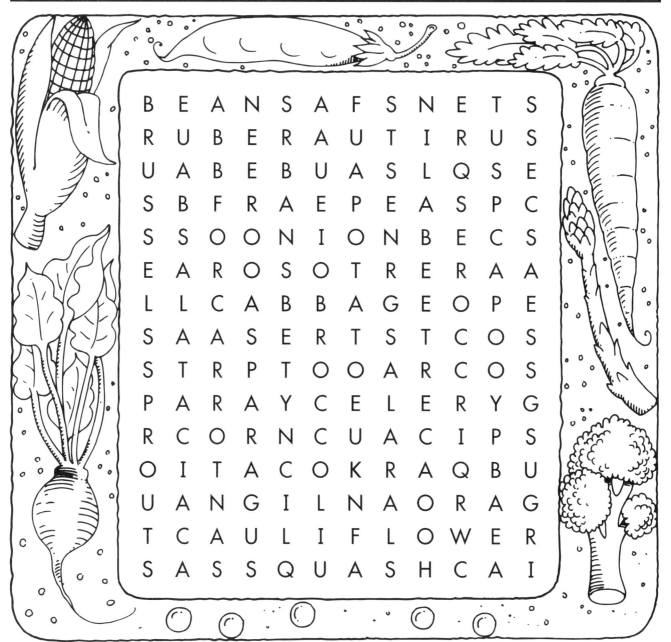

```
B E A N S A F S N E T S
R U B E R A U T I R U S
U A B E B U A S L Q S E
S B F R A E P E A S P C
S S O O N I O N B E C S
E A R O S O T R E R A A
L L C A B B A G E O P E
S A A S E R T S T C O S
S T R P T O O A R C O S
P A R A Y C E L E R Y G
R C O R N C U A C I P S
O I T A C O K R A Q B U
U A N G I L N A O R A G
T C A U L I F L O W E R
S A S S Q U A S H C A I
```

Word Games • 2–3 © 2005 Creative Teaching Press

Name _____ Date _____

Weather Search

Science, Spelling, and Vocabulary

Find and circle the weather words hidden in the puzzle. Words can be found going from left to right and top to bottom.

cloud	hail	rain	dew	hurricane
snow	drizzle	icicle	thunder	fog
lightning	tornado	frost	mist	wind

```
M  S  D  R  I  Z  Z  L  E
I  R  F  R  O  S  T  I  E
S  N  O  W  N  F  O  G  U
T  H  U  N  D  E  R  H  R
I  C  I  C  L  E  N  T  C
H  U  R  R  I  C  A  N  E
A  Z  C  L  O  U  D  I  L
I  R  A  I  N  O  O  N  A
L  W  I  N  D  E  W  G  L
```

City Search

Social Studies, Spelling, and Vocabulary

Find and circle the names of the United States cities hidden in the puzzle. Words can be found going from left to right and top to bottom.

Austin	Frankfort	Madison	Baton Rouge	Hartford
Phoenix	Boston	Helena	Sacramento	Charleston
Juneau	Seattle	Columbia	Lansing	Topeka

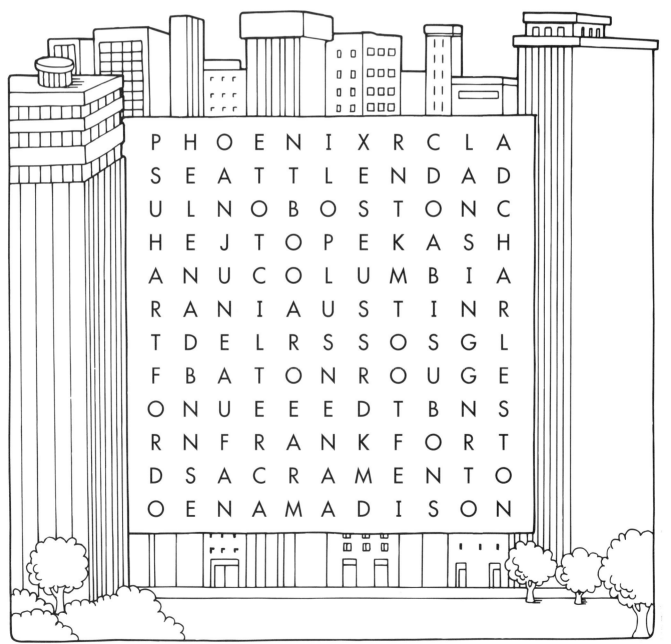

P H O E N I X R C L A
S E A T T L E N D A D
U L N O B O S T O N C
H E J T O P E K A S H
A N U C O L U M B I A
R A N I A U S T I N R
T D E L R S S O S G L
F B A T O N R O U G E
O N U E E E D T B N S
R N F R A N K F O R T
D S A C R A M E N T O
O E N A M A D I S O N

Word Games • 2–3 © 2005 Creative Teaching Press

Name _____ Date _____

Community Helper Search

Social Studies, Spelling, and Vocabulary

Find and circle the names of the community helpers hidden in the puzzle. Words can be found going from left to right and top to bottom.

baker	dentist	librarian	banker	doctor
plumber	bus driver	firefighter	police officer	carpenter
gardener	teacher	coach	judge	truck driver

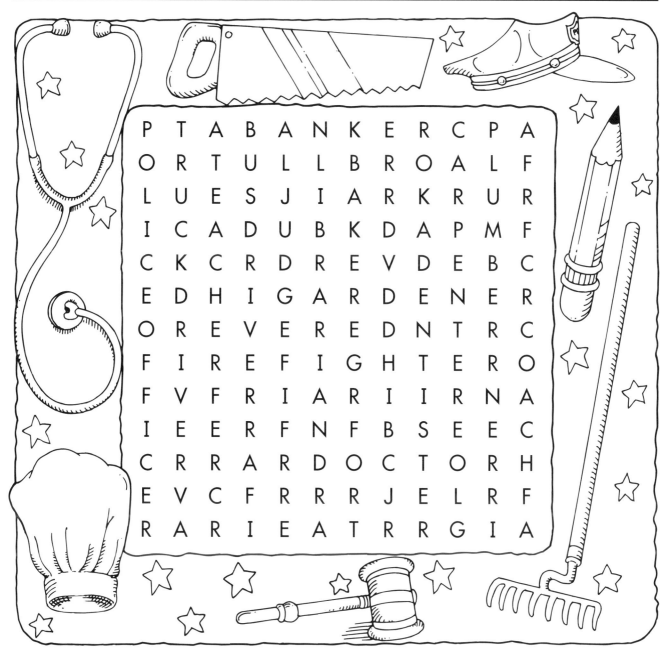

```
P  T  A  B  A  N  K  E  R  C  P  A
O  R  T  U  L  L  B  R  O  A  L  F
L  U  E  S  J  I  A  R  K  R  U  R
I  C  A  D  U  B  K  D  A  P  M  F
C  K  C  R  D  R  E  V  D  E  B  C
E  D  H  I  G  A  R  D  E  N  E  R
O  R  E  V  E  R  E  D  N  T  R  C
F  I  R  E  F  I  G  H  T  E  R  O
F  V  F  R  I  A  R  I  I  R  N  A
I  E  E  R  F  N  F  B  S  E  E  C
C  R  R  A  R  D  O  C  T  O  R  H
E  V  C  F  R  R  R  J  E  L  R  F
R  A  R  I  E  A  T  R  R  G  I  A
```

State Search

Social Studies, Spelling, and Vocabulary

Find and circle the names of the states hidden in the puzzle. Words can be found going from left to right and top to bottom.

Alaska	Maryland	Tennessee	Delaware	Mississippi
Texas	Hawaii	Montana	Utah	Idaho
Ohio	Vermont	Iowa	Oregon	Wisconsin

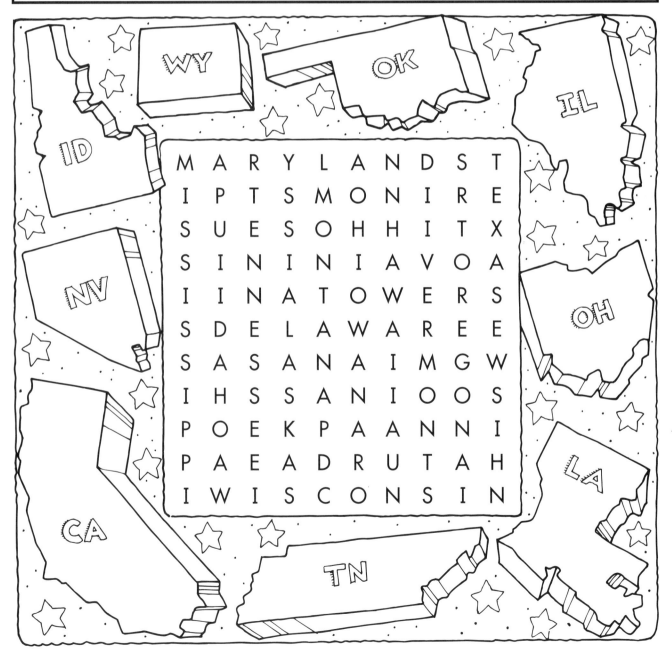

```
M A R Y L A N D S T
I P T S M O N I R E
S U E S O H H I T X
S I N I N I A V O A
I I N A T O W E R S
S D E L A W A R E E
S A S A N A I M G W
I H S S A N I O O S
P O E K P A A N N I
P A E A D R U T A H
I W I S C O N S I N
```

Word Games • 2–3 © 2005 Creative Teaching Press

Tolerance Search

Social Studies, Spelling, and Vocabulary

Find and circle the words related to tolerance hidden in the puzzle. Words can be found going from left to right and top to bottom.

acceptance	forgiveness	respect	caring	helping
responsibility	compassion	honesty	sharing	compromise
kindness	tolerance	courage	patience	understanding

Name _____ Date _____

Transportation Search

Social Studies, Spelling, and Vocabulary

Find and circle the transportation words hidden in the puzzle. Words can be found going from left to right and top to bottom.

airplane	bus	streetcar	ambulance	canoe
taxicab	automobile	motorcycle	train	bicycle
rowboat	trolley	blimp	skateboard	truck

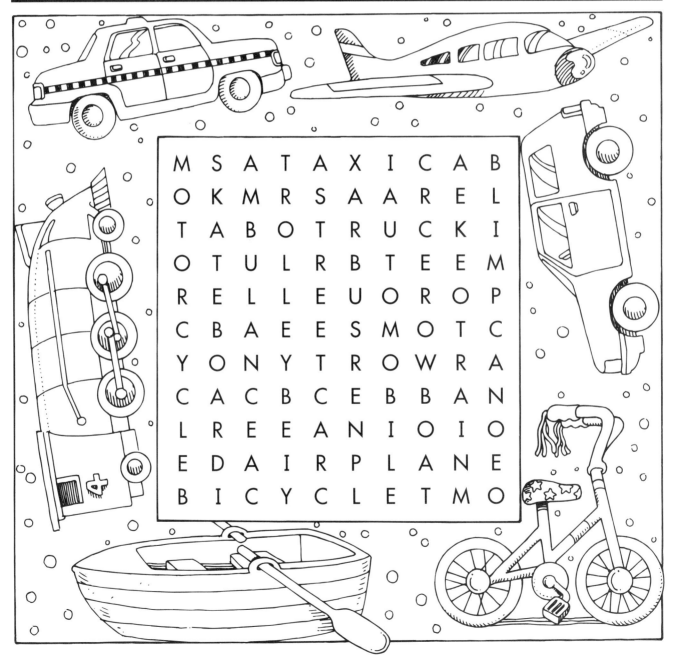

M S A T A X I C A B
O K M R S A A R E L
T A B O T R U C K I
O T U L R B T E E M
R E L L E U O R O P
C B A E E S M O T C
Y O N Y T R O W R A
C A C B C E B B A N
L R E E A N I O I O
E D A I R P L A N E
B I C Y C L E T M O

Word Games • 2–3 © 2005 Creative Teaching Press

Name _____ Date _____

Valentine's Day Search

Holidays, Spelling, and Vocabulary

Find and circle the Valentine's Day words hidden in the puzzle. Words can be found going from left to right and top to bottom.

arrow	cookies	lace	bow	cupid
love	candy	February	red	cards
flowers	sweetheart	caring	hearts	valentines

```
S V F L O W E R S
W A E R H C C C B
E L B O E A A O O
E E R C A R R O W
T N U A R D C K C
H T A R T S U I A
E I R I S L P E N
A N Y N E A I S D
R E D G L C D E Y
T S L O V E S U I
```

Word Games • 2–3 © 2005 Creative Teaching Press

Thanksgiving Search

Holidays, Spelling, and Vocabulary

Find and circle the Thanksgiving words hidden in the puzzle. Words can be found going from left to right and top to bottom.

corn	gathering	Pilgrims	cranberries	harvest
fall	Indians	pumpkin	Plymouth Rock	feast
Mayflower	stuffing	football	November	turkey

P F O O T B A L L S B
L O H A R V E S T R M
Y M R F E A S T U C L
M A P G P N N U R O P
O Y U A S G O F K R I
U F M T F V V F E N L
T L P H A A E I Y U G
H O K E L I M N G I R
R W I R L R B G O S I
O E N I U O E N M N M
C R A N B E R R I E S
K H E G I N D I A N S

Word Games • 2–3 © 2005 Creative Teaching Press

Name _____   Date _____

Hanukkah Search

Holidays, Spelling, and Vocabulary

Find and circle the Hanukkah words hidden in the puzzle. Words can be found going from left to right and top to bottom.

candles	oil	miracle	dreidel	latkes
Hanukkah	eight	lights	presents	festival
Maccabees	songs	gelt	menorah	temple

```
G  T  E  M  P  L  E  A  R  S
O  I  L  I  G  H  T  S  S  O
D  A  C  R  H  M  K  F  P  N
L  F  R  A  H  E  N  T  R  G
C  E  A  C  A  N  D  L  E  S
G  S  S  L  N  O  R  L  S  E
E  T  A  E  U  R  E  A  E  I
L  I  M  A  K  A  I  T  N  G
T  V  L  T  K  H  D  K  T  H
M  A  C  C  A  B  E  E  S  T
M  L  R  R  H  L  L  S  E  M
```

Name _____ Date _____

Christmas Search

Holidays, Spelling, and Vocabulary

Find and circle the Christmas words hidden in the puzzle. Words can be found going from left to right and top to bottom.

angel	elf	Santa Claus	candles	holly
sleigh	mistletoe	candy canes	stockings	carols
ornaments	toys	December	reindeer	wreath

```
E  L  F  C  S  G  I  A  C  Y
S  S  T  O  C  K  I  N  G  S
D  E  C  E  M  B  E  R  M  A
T  C  A  R  O  L  S  E  I  N
O  R  N  A  M  E  N  T  S  T
Y  D  D  A  N  G  E  L  T  A
S  S  L  E  I  G  H  R  L  C
W  R  E  A  T  H  L  Y  E  L
T  I  S  H  O  L  L  Y  T  A
R  E  I  N  D  E  E  R  O  U
C  A  N  D  Y  C  A  N  E  S
```

Name _____

Date _____

Short Vowel Words

Phonics

For each category write a word that begins with the letter on the left. Score one point for each correct answer. Earn five bonus points for any category where you have no incorrect answers or blanks.

Letter	Short a Sound (cat)	Short e Sound (let)	Short i Sound (fig)	Short o Sound (dog)	Short u Sound (rug)	Score
B						
H						
P						
T						
M						
					Total	
					Bonus	
					Final Score	

Long Vowel Words

Phonics

For each category write a word that begins with the letter on the left. Score one point for each correct answer. Earn five bonus points for any category where you have no incorrect answers or blanks.

Letter	Long a Sound (haste)	Long e Sound (tree)	Long i Sound (ride)	Long o Sound (home)	Long u Sound (tune)	Score
B						
F						
M						
R						
S						
					Total	
					Bonus	
					Final Score	

Word Games • 2–3 © 2005 Creative Teaching Press

Fun with Words

Phonics and Vocabulary

For each category write a word that begins with the letter on the left. Score one point for each correct answer.
Earn five bonus points for any category where you have no incorrect answers or blanks.

Letter	A One-Syllable Word (toy)	A Two-Syllable Word (bottle)	A Plural Word (houses)	A Compound Word (homework)	A Noun (flower)	Score
A						
M						
N						
O						
W						

	Total	
	Bonus	
	Final Score	

Colors

Phonics and Vocabulary

For each category write a word that is usually that color and begins with the letter on the left. Score one point for each correct answer. Earn five bonus points for any category where you have no incorrect answers or blanks.

Letter	Red	Yellow	Blue	Green	Brown	Score
B						
G						
D						
L						
F						
					Total	
					Bonus	
					Final Score	

Name _____

Date _____

Around the House

Phonics and Vocabulary

For each category write the name of an object found there that begins with the letter on the left. Score one point for each correct answer. Earn five bonus points for any category where you have no incorrect answers or blanks.

Letter	In the Kitchen	In the Living Room	In the Bathroom	In the Bedroom	In the Family Room	Score
T						
C						
B						
S						
R						
					Total	
					Bonus	
					Final Score	

Plants and Animals

Phonics and Vocabulary

For each category write a word that begins with the letter on the left. Score one point for each correct answer. Earn five bonus points for any category where you have no incorrect answers or blanks. Use a dictionary if you need help finding a word for any category.

Letter	Mammal	Bird	Fish	Flower	Tree	Score
B						
T						
D						
P						
G						
					Total	
					Bonus	
					Final Score	

People

Phonics and Vocabulary

For each category write a word that begins with the letter on the left. Score one point for each correct answer. Earn five bonus points for any category where you have no incorrect answers or blanks. Use a dictionary if you need help finding a word for any category.

Letter	Boy's Name	Girl's Name	Famous Person (last name)	Community Helper	Actor or Actress (last name)	Score
A						
F						
L						
N						
C						
					Total	
					Bonus	
					Final Score	

Name _____

Date _____

Leisure Time

Phonics and Vocabulary

For each category write a word that begins with the letter on the left. You may skip the first word if it is *a*, *an*, or *the*. Score one point for each correct answer. Earn five bonus points for any category where you have no incorrect answers or blanks.

Letter	Television Show	Sport or Game	Book	Song	Movie	Score
R						
G						
B						
O						
P						
					Total	
					Bonus	
					Final Score	

Name _____

Date _____

On the Menu

Phonics and Vocabulary

For each category write a word that begins with the letter on the left. Score one point for each correct answer. Earn five bonus points for any category where you have no incorrect answers or blanks. Use a dictionary if you need help finding a word for any category.

Letter	Fruit	Vegetable	Dessert	Main Course	Drink	Score
M						
C						
P						
B						
S						
					Total	
					Bonus	
					Final Score	

Name _____

Date _____

Shopping Spree

Phonics and Vocabulary

For each category write the name of something that you would buy at that store and that begins with the letter on the left. Score one point for each correct answer. Earn five bonus points for any category where you have no incorrect answers or blanks. Use a dictionary if you need help finding a word for any category.

Letter	Department Store	Furniture Store	Office Supply Store	Toy Store	Grocery Store	Score
C						
P						
S						
T						
D						
					Total	
					Bonus	
					Final Score	

Name _____ Date _____

Rhyming Crisscross

Rhyming, Phonics, Vocabulary, and Spelling

Use the clues to write two words that rhyme in the boxes going across and down. Put one letter in each box. The first one has been done for you.

Across	**Down**

1. an insect | a cup

2. fright | close by

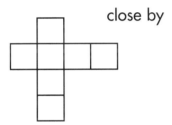

3. a bird's mouth | seven days

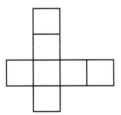

4. a season | helps a bird fly

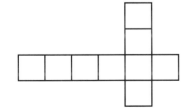

Across	**Down**

5. a bird's home | an exam

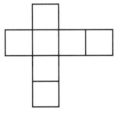

6. opposite of **bride** | used to sweep the floor

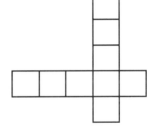

7. a reptile | used to gather leaves

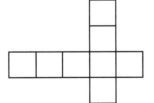

8. opposite of **work** | remain

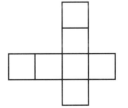

Word Games • 2–3 © 2005 Creative Teaching Press

Name _____ Date _____

More Rhyming Crisscross

Rhyming, Phonics, Vocabulary, and Spelling

Use the clues to write two words that rhyme in the boxes going across and down. Put one letter in each box. The first one has been done for you.

Across	Down	Across	Down

1. 24 hours   a blue bird

5. a baby sheep   fruit spread

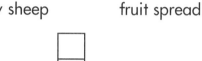

2. a small tree branch   large

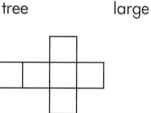

6. not written on   a place where money is kept

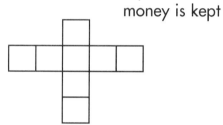

3. a place to skate   a bad smell

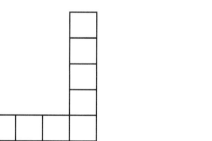

7. little   a round toy

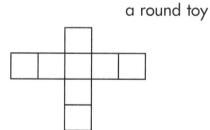

4. duck's sound   a bag

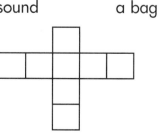

8. opposite of **queen**   jewelry worn on the finger

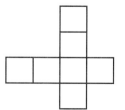

Word Games • 2–3 © 2005 Creative Teaching Press

Verb Tense Crisscross

Verb Tenses, Vocabulary, and Spelling

Use the clues to write the past tense of each verb in the boxes going across and down. Put one letter in each box. The first one has been done for you.

Across	**Down**		**Across**	**Down**
1. run	eat		**5.** choose	speak

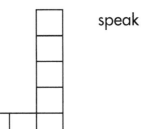

Across	**Down**		**Across**	**Down**
2. drink	forget		**6.** throw	shrink

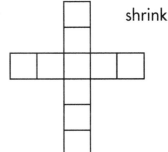

Across	**Down**		**Across**	**Down**
3. freeze	shake		**7.** ride	break

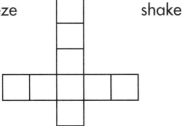

Across	**Down**		**Across**	**Down**
4. write	wear		**8.** go	fly

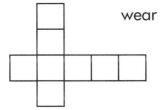

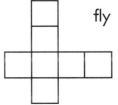

Name _____   Date _____

Synonym Crisscross

Synonyms, Vocabulary, and Spelling

Use the clues to write two words that have similar meanings in the boxes going across and down. Put one letter in each box. The first one has been done for you.

Across	Down	Across	Down

1. genuine   hurry

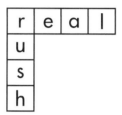

2. repair   close by

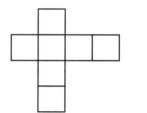

3. mighty   damp

4. happen   imitate

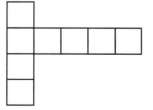

5. sensible   whole

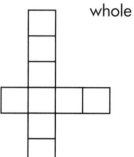

6. area   pain

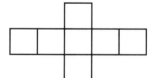

7. gleam   assist

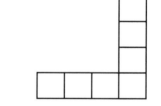

8. govern   mix

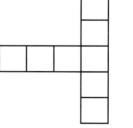

Word Games • 2–3 © 2005 Creative Teaching Press

Name _____   Date _____

Opposite Word Crisscross

Antonyms, Vocabulary, and Spelling

Use the clues to write two words that have opposite meanings in the boxes going across and down. Put one letter in each box. The first one has been done for you.

Across	Down
1. hot	hard

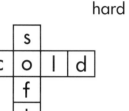

Across	Down
2. all	begin

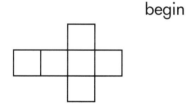

Across	Down
3. best	bottom

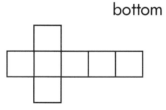

Across	Down
4. dirty	front

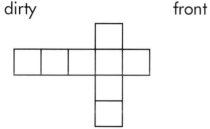

Across	Down
5. ugly	before

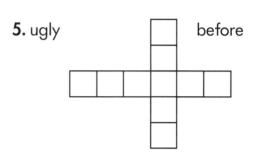

Across	Down
6. different	many

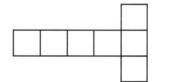

Across	Down
7. low	noisy

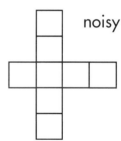

Across	Down
8. thin	tame

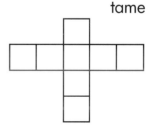

Name _____ Date _____

Measurement Crossword Puzzle

Measurement, Vocabulary, and Spelling

All the words in the clue box are measurement terms. Write each word in the crossword puzzle. Put one letter in each box. One word has been written for you. *(Hint: Write the longer words first.)*

Clue Box

3-letter words
ton
cup

4-letter words
inch
yard
pint

5-letter words
ounce
pound
quart

6-letter word
gallon

8-letter word
teaspoon

10-letter word
tablespoon

Word Games • 2–3 © 2005 Creative Teaching Press

Zoo Crossword Puzzle

Vocabulary and Spelling

Write each animal name in the crossword puzzle. Put one letter in each box. One word has been written for you. *(Hint: Write the longer words first.)*

Clue Box

3-letter word
gnu

4-letter words
lion
seal

5-letter words
tiger
sloth

6-letter words
gibbon
weasel

7-letter words
cheetah
giraffe
gorilla

8-letter word
mongoose

10-letter word
chimpanzee

g
n
u

Collection Crossword Puzzle

Vocabulary and Spelling

All the words in the clue box are names of things that you can collect. Write each word in the crossword puzzle. Put one letter in each box. One word has been written for you. *(Hint: Write the longer words first.)*

Clue Box

4-letter word
pins

5-letter words
dolls
books
rocks
coins

6-letter words
shells
stamps

7-letter words
buttons
marbles
posters

8-letter word
stickers

9-letter word
postcards

10-letter word
autographs

Word Games • 2–3 © 2005 Creative Teaching Press

Things with Holes Crossword Puzzle

Vocabulary and Spelling

All the words in the clue box are names of things that have holes. Write each word in the crossword puzzle. Put one letter in each box. One word has been written for you. *(Hint: Write the longer words first.)*

Clue Box

<u>3-letter word</u>
net

<u>4-letter words</u>
lock
nose

<u>5-letter words</u>
bagel
straw

<u>6-letter words</u>
button
funnel
grater

<u>7-letter word</u>
chimney

<u>8-letter words</u>
strainer
scissors
doughnut

<u>9-letter word</u>
handcuffs

Noun Crossword Puzzle #1

Nouns, Vocabulary, and Spelling

> A **noun** is the name of a person, place, or thing.

Write the noun that best matches each definition to complete the crossword puzzle. Put one letter in each box. Use the words in the word bank if you need help. The first one has been done for you.

acorn	colt	error	forest	globe
hoof	neighbor	opera	quarrel	rage

Across
2. foot of a cow
4. uncontrolled anger; fury
6. a young male horse
8. a play that is sung
10. a person who lives near another

Down
1. a round model of the earth
3. large woods
5. a mistake
7. nut or fruit of an oak tree
9. an argument

Word Games • 2–3 © 2005 Creative Teaching Press

Name _____ Date _____

Noun Crossword Puzzle #2

Nouns, Vocabulary, and Spelling

> A **noun** is the name of a person, place, or thing.

Write the noun that best matches each definition to complete the crossword puzzle. Put one letter in each box. Use the words in the word bank if you need help. The first one has been done for you.

ankle	aorta	blaze	edge	kettle
lava	lizard	mate	plan	valley

Across

2. one of a pair
4. a bright flame or fire
6. lowland between hills or mountains
8. the main artery of the body
10. a way of doing something that has been thought out ahead of time
12. a border or margin

Down

1. a metal container for boiling or cooking
3. hot, melted rock from a volcano
5. a reptile with scales
8. the joint that connects the foot and lower leg

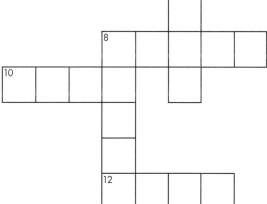

Name _____ Date _____

Verb Crossword Puzzle

Verbs, Vocabulary, and Spelling

A **verb** is a word that expresses action (e.g., *ran*, *skipped*, or *sang*). A verb can also tell the condition of someone or something (e.g., *became*, *am*, *is*, and *are*).

Write the verb that best matches each definition to complete the crossword puzzle. Put one letter in each box. Use the words in the word bank if you need help. The first one has been done for you.

cause	extend	give	lend	relax
select	twinkle	unite	urge	warn

Across
2. to tell of a danger
4. to make longer; stretched out
6. to become less tense; loosen up
8. to make happen
10. to present something to another person

Down
1. to sparkle
3. to combine
5. to let someone use something for a while
7. to choose or pick out
9. to advise someone, in a strong way, to do something

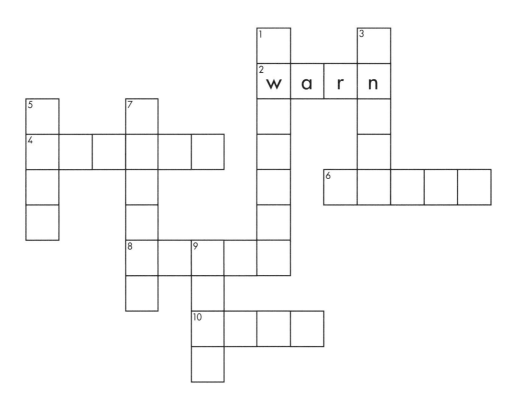

Word Games • 2–3 © 2005 Creative Teaching Press

Name _____ Date _____

Adjective Crossword Puzzle

Adjectives, Vocabulary, and Spelling

An **adjective** is a word that describes a noun or a pronoun. An adjective tells how many, what kind, or which one.

Write the adjective that best matches each definition to complete the crossword puzzle. Put one letter in each box. Use the words in the word bank if you need help. The first one has been done for you.

careful	cruel	dual	flimsy	hardy
ignorant	imaginary	lively	reliable	temporary

Across
2. full of life or energy
4. not real
6. cautious
8. causing pain or suffering
10. last only for a short time; not permanent

Down
1. capable of being trusted
3. not aware of
5. strong
7. easily damaged; weak
9. made up of two parts

Word Games • 2–3 © 2005 Creative Teaching Press

Name _____ Date _____

Plurals Crossword Puzzle

Plurals, Vocabulary, and Spelling

A **noun** is the name of a person, place, or thing. A noun that is **singular** names only one person, place, or thing. A noun that is **plural** names more than one.

Write the plural form of each singular noun to complete the crossword puzzle. Put one letter in each box. The first one has been done for you.

Across
- **3.** fox
- **5.** baby
- **7.** child
- **9.** mouse
- **11.** calf
- **13.** goose
- **15.** half
- **16.** tomato

Down
- **1.** woman
- **2.** donkey
- **4.** tool
- **6.** bunny
- **8.** hero
- **10.** cargo
- **12.** alto
- **14.** man

Word Games • 2–3 © 2005 Creative Teaching Press

Name _____ Date _____

Eat It, Wear It, or Plant It?

Vocabulary and Classifying

Decide if you would eat, wear, or plant each of the things in the box. Write each word under the correct heading. You should have four words in each category. Use a dictionary if you need help.

custard	goulash	cardigan	tofu
violet	cape	marigold	stew
vest	iris	scarf	daffodil

 **Eat It**   **Wear It**

_____   _____

_____   _____

_____   _____

_____   _____

Plant It

_____

_____

_____

_____

Add two or more words of your own under each heading.

Word Games • 2–3 © 2005 Creative Teaching Press

Name _____ Date _____

Land, Sea, or Air Animal?

Vocabulary and Classifying

Decide if each animal in the box walks on land, swims in the sea, or flies in the air. Write each word under the correct heading. You should have four words in each category. Use a dictionary if you need help.

hawk	cheetah	ocelot	mackerel
beagle	perch	bass	camel
bee	raven	minnow	robin

On Land

_____

_____

_____

_____

_____

In the Sea

_____

_____

_____

_____

_____

In the Air

_____

_____

_____

_____

_____

Add two or more words of your own under each heading.

Name _____ Date _____

Mammal, Fish, or Reptile?

Vocabulary and Classifying

Decide if each animal in the box is a mammal, fish, or reptile. Write each word under the correct heading. You should have four words in each category. Use a dictionary if you need help.

alligator	turtle	trout	marlin
cod	stingray	snake	yak
otter	hyena	mole	tortoise

 Mammal

 Fish

_____
_____
_____
_____

_____
_____
_____
_____

 Reptile

_____
_____
_____
_____

Add two or more words of your own under each heading.

Word Games • 2–3 © 2005 Creative Teaching Press

Fruit, Vegetable, or Tree?

Vocabulary and Classifying

Decide if each word in the box is the name of a fruit, vegetable, or tree. Write each word under the correct heading. You should have four words in each category. Use a dictionary if you need help.

sequoia	strawberry	asparagus	spinach
kiwi	cauliflower	spruce	magnolia
broccoli	cedar	watermelon	grape

Fruit

_____

_____

_____

_____

_____

_____

Vegetable

_____

_____

_____

_____

_____

_____

Tree

_____

_____

_____

_____

_____

_____

Add two or more words of your own under each heading.

Noun, Verb, or Adjective?

Vocabulary, Parts of Speech, and Classifying

Decide if each underlined word in the phrases in the box is used as a noun, a verb, or an adjective. Write the underlined word under the correct heading. You should have four words in each category.

was going	asked for help	frisky puppy	a great game
sliced the meat	gloomy night	she spoke	he ran
fast car	a large crowd	lazy lizard	full of joy

Noun

_____

_____

_____

_____

_____

Verb

_____

_____

_____

_____

_____

Adjective

_____

_____

_____

_____

_____

_____

Add two or more words of your own under each heading.

Feet, Head, or Body?

Vocabulary and Classifying

Decide if each thing in the box is worn on the feet, the head, or somewhere else on the body. Write each word under the correct heading. You should have five words in each category. Use a dictionary if you need help.

sombrero	crown	bonnet	cap	helmet
robe	cleats	sneakers	boots	suspenders
slippers	cloak	tuxedo	jacket	sandals

Worn on the Feet

_____

_____

_____

_____

_____

Worn on the Head

_____

_____

_____

_____

_____

Worn Somewhere Else on the Body

_____

_____

_____

_____

_____

Word Games • 2–3 © 2005 Creative Teaching Press

Name _____ Date _____

Travel by Land, Water, or Air?

Vocabulary and Classifying

Decide if each thing in the box is a way of traveling on land, on water, or in the air. Write each word under the correct heading. You should have five words in each category. Use a dictionary if you need help.

helicopter	blimp	submarine	jet	yacht
tricycle	kayak	scooter	raft	ferry
tractor	moped	rocket	bus	hot air balloon

Travel by Land

_____

_____

_____

_____

_____

Travel by Water

_____

_____

_____

_____

_____

Travel by Air

_____

_____

_____

_____

_____

Word Games • 2–3 © 2005 Creative Teaching Press

Name _____ Date _____

Hold, Measure, or Read?

Vocabulary and Classifying

Decide if each item in the box is something that holds things, something that is used for measuring, or something that you read. Write each word under the correct heading. You should have five words in each category. Use a dictionary if you need help.

bowl	basket	hamper	vase	encyclopedia
almanac	clock	ruler	brochure	magazine
thermometer	catalog	bucket	odometer	speedometer

Items That Hold Things

_____

_____

_____

_____

_____

Things That Are Used for Measuring

_____

_____

_____

_____

_____

Something That Is Read

_____

_____

_____

_____

_____

Word Games • 2–3 © 2005 Creative Teaching Press

Name _____ Date _____

Play It, Sing It, or Dance It?

Vocabulary and Classifying

Decide if each item in the box is a musical instrument you play, something you sing, or a kind of dance. Write each word under the correct heading. You should have five words in each category. Use a dictionary if you need help.

ballet	chorus	lullaby	tuba	tune
flute	tango	opera	polka	oboe
harp	clarinet	hula	melody	waltz

A Musical Instrument

_____

_____

_____

_____

_____

Things You Can Sing

_____

_____

_____

_____

_____

Kinds of Dances

_____

_____

_____

_____

_____

Name _____ Date _____

Football, Baseball, or Basketball?

Vocabulary and Classifying

Decide if the words in the box are terms used in football, baseball, or basketball. Write each term under the correct heading. You should have five words in each category. Use a dictionary if you need help.

kickoff	huddle	punt	tackle	fly
rebound	pitch	hoop	touchdown	diamond
bunt	jump shot	walk	dribble	court

Football Terms

_____

_____

_____

_____

Baseball Terms

_____

_____

_____

_____

Basketball Terms

_____

_____

_____

_____

Word Games • 2–3 © 2005 Creative Teaching Press

Name _____ Date _____

Riddle #1

Language Skills

What did the archaeologist say to the mummy?

Follow the directions below to solve the riddle. The first step has been done for you.

LAZY	~~CALVES~~	THERE	NOSE
NERVOUS	LIBRARIAN	~~CITIES~~	I
HELPFUL	DIG	MOUTH	NURSE
YOU	THEY'RE	EYE	~~WISHES~~

1. Cross off all words that are plurals.
2. Cross off all words that name a part of the face.
3. Cross off all words that are homophones for the word **their**.
4. Cross off all words that are adjectives.
5. Cross off all words that are the names of community helpers.

The words that have NOT been crossed off are the answer to the riddle.

- Draw a circle around these words.
- Start in the top left-hand corner of the puzzle.
- Read the circled words going *across* each row.
- Write the answer to the riddle on the line below.

_____

Word Games • 2–3 © 2005 Creative Teaching Press

Riddle #2

Language Skills

For what vegetable do people throw away the outside, cook the inside, eat the outside, and then throw away the inside?

Follow the directions below to solve the riddle. The first step has been done for you.

BEETLE	MICE	AIRPLANE	BEETS
RUNNING	PEAS	PROP	WOMEN
CORN	AWAY	ON	HOUSES
~~EXCUSE~~	FORGIVE	LADYBUG	THE
~~PLUMP~~	BABOON	COB	~~MOM~~

1. Cross off all words that begin and end with the same letter.
2. Cross off all words that are verbs.
3. Cross off all words that are the names of insects.
4. Cross off all words that come <u>before</u> the word **baby** in the dictionary.
5. Cross off all words that are plurals.

The words that have NOT been crossed off are the answer to the riddle.

• Draw a circle around these words.
• Start in the top left-hand corner of the puzzle.
• Read the circled words going *across* each row.
• Write the answer to the riddle on the line below.

_____

Word Games • 2–3 © 2005 Creative Teaching Press

Name _____   Date _____

Riddle #3

Language Skills

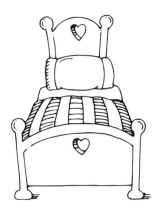

What kind of bed is only good for three seasons?

Follow the directions below to solve the riddle.

BUS	DAD	BETTER	ORANGE
BICYCLE	ONE	MILK	TIGER
BLUE	CAR	WITH	DEED
PAPER	BUTTER	TABLE	NO
DID	SODA	SPRINGS	PURPLE

1. Cross off all words that have two of the same consonant next to each other.
2. Cross off all words that start and end with the letter **d**.
3. Cross off all words that are names of colors.
4. Cross off all words that have exactly five letters.
5. Cross off all words that are names of drinks.
6. Cross off all words that are things with wheels.

The words that have NOT been crossed off are the answer to the riddle.

- Draw a circle around these words.
- Start in the top left-hand corner of the puzzle.
- Read the circled words going *across* each row.
- Write the answer to the riddle on the lines below.

_____

_____

Word Games • 2–3 © 2005 Creative Teaching Press

Riddle #4

Language Skills

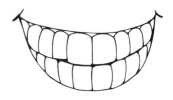

What has lots of teeth but can't chew?

Follow the directions below to solve the riddle.

HOP	BIRD	STOP	BASKETBALL
SHIRT	TENT	AIRPLANE	A
SEED	NECKTIE	TREAT	MOON
THAT	SOCCER	MOTH	SHOP
SHOES	KITE	BROOM	COMB

1. Cross off all words that have two of the same vowel next to each other.
2. Cross off all words that start and end with the letter **t**.
3. Cross off all words that are names of things people wear.
4. Cross off all words that are names of sports.
5. Cross off all words that rhyme with the word **top**.
6. Cross off all words that are things that can fly.

The words that have NOT been crossed off are the answer to the riddle.

- Draw a circle around these words.
- Start in the top left-hand corner of the puzzle.
- Read the circled words going *across* each row.
- Write the answer to the riddle on the line below.

_____

Word Games • 2–3 © 2005 Creative Teaching Press

Riddle #5

Language Skills

Why can't leopards play hide-and-seek?

Follow the directions below to solve the riddle.

SCISSORS	ZOO	LEMON	ICE
THEY	TOGETHER	SNOW	FIVE
DELICIOUS	KNIFE	SUN	YES
WERE	ARE	FIFTEEN	VERY
ALWAYS	NEEDLE	SPOTTED	FOUR

1. Cross off all words that are names of things that are yellow.
2. Cross off all words that have exactly three syllables.
3. Cross off all words that are names of things that are cold.
4. Cross off all words that are names of numbers.
5. Cross off all words that come <u>after</u> the word **uncle** in the dictionary.
6. Cross off all words that are names of things that are sharp.

The words that have NOT been crossed off are the answer to the riddle.

• Draw a circle around these words.
• Start in the top left-hand corner of the puzzle.
• Read the circled words going *across* each row.
• Write the answer to the riddle on the lines below.

_____

_____

Riddle #6

Language Skills

Why did the squirrel stop arguing with the porcupine?

Follow the directions below to solve the riddle.

LENTIL	BROOK	CHECKERS	LION
HOMEWORK	APPLE	DELICIOUS	HIGH
CAB	NECKTIE	CHESS	EXCITING
SHE	CARDS	GOT	ZEBRA
THE	SAILBOAT	OLD	POINT

1. Cross off all words that are compound words.
2. Cross off all words that are adjectives.
3. Cross off all words that are names of games people play.
4. Cross off all words that are names of zoo animals.
5. Cross off all words that come <u>before</u> the word **cable** in the dictionary.
6. Cross off all words that begin and end with the same letter.

The words that have NOT been crossed off are the answer to the riddle.

• Draw a circle around these words.
• Start in the top left-hand corner of the puzzle.
• Read the circled words going *across* each row.
• Write the answer to the riddle on the lines below.

_____

_____

Word Games • 2–3 © 2005 Creative Teaching Press

Riddle #7

Language Skills

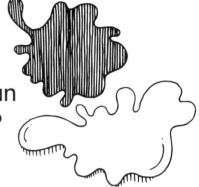

What's black when it's clean and white when it's dirty?

Follow the directions below to solve the riddle.

CAN'T	GLOVES	ADDRESS	A
PANSY	TREAT	WHERE	RINGS
BEAT	MEANING	HAVEN'T	YOUTH
SUCCESS	TULIP	MITT	FEAT
CARNATION	SHOULDN'T	BLACKBOARD	HEAT

1. Cross off all words that rhyme with the word **wheat**.
2. Cross off all words that have exactly seven letters.
3. Cross off all words that are things people wear on their hands.
4. Cross off all words that are names of flowers.
5. Cross off all words that come <u>after</u> the word **water** in the dictionary.
6. Cross off all words that are contractions.

The words that have NOT been crossed off are the answer to the riddle.

- Draw a circle around these words.
- Start in the top left-hand corner of the puzzle.
- Read the circled words going *across* each row.
- Write the answer to the riddle on the line below.

_____

Name _____ Date _____

Riddle #8

Language Skills

What do automobiles do at a disco?

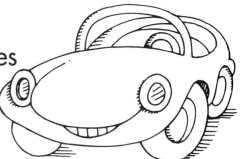

Follow the directions below to solve the riddle.

HAIR	RABBITS	CAN	THEY
BROWN	FIFTY	FRUIT	PINK
HAMSTERS	GRAY	FAIR	WEAR
FOR	PIZZA	DOGS	BRAKE
DANCE	WHO	MEAT	NINETEEN

1. Cross off all words that rhyme with the word **care**.
2. Cross off all words that are names of numbers.
3. Cross off all words that are things people eat.
4. Cross off all words that are names of animals people keep as pets.
5. Cross off all words that have exactly three letters.
6. Cross off all words that are names of colors.

The words that have NOT been crossed off are the answer to the riddle.

- Draw a circle around these words.
- Start in the top left-hand corner of the puzzle.
- Read the circled words going *across* each row.
- Write the answer to the riddle on the line below.

_____

Word Games • 2–3 © 2005 Creative Teaching Press

Riddle #9

Language Skills

On what do astronauts like to eat?

Follow the directions below to solve the riddle.

CRAYON	FROM	PENCIL	FREIGHT
CEDAR	RICHER	CYMBALS	GIRL
DRUMS	TIME	APARTMENT	ELM
FLYING	BIRCH	WEIGHT	RANGER
PEN	CLARINET	SAUCERS	BACKS

1. Cross off all words that have an **ei** spelling.
2. Cross off all words that have exactly four letters.
3. Cross off all words that are things people use for writing or drawing.
4. Cross off all words that are the names of trees.
5. Cross off all words that come <u>before</u> the word **better** in the dictionary.
6. Cross off all words that are the names of instruments in a band.
7. Cross off all words that start and end with the letter **r**.

The words that have NOT been crossed off are the answer to the riddle.

- Draw a circle around these words.
- Start in the top left-hand corner of the puzzle.
- Read the circled words going *across* each row.
- Write the answer to the riddle on the line below.

_____

Riddle #10

Language Skills

What did the baby banana say to his father?

Follow the directions below to solve the riddle.

NEWSPAPER	ABOUT	DIDN'T	MAINE
NIECE	DRIP	FLOOR	I
FRIEND	WASN'T	DO	MAGAZINE
DRIVE	TWO	SARAH	MORE
NOT	TOO	BOOK	THEY'RE
PEEL	FOUR	PIECE	VERY
STEPHEN	ABOARD	WELL	ATLANTIC

1. Cross off all words that are contractions.
2. Cross off all words that rhyme with the word **door**.
3. Cross off all words that are proper nouns.
4. Cross off all words that have an **ie** spelling.
5. Cross off all words that are homophones for the word **to**.
6. Cross off all words that begin with the first two letters of the alphabet.
7. Cross off all words that are things people read.
8. Cross off all words that begin with the **dr** blend.

The words that have NOT been crossed off are the answer to the riddle.

- Draw a circle around these words.
- Start in the top left-hand corner of the puzzle.
- Read the circled words going *across* each row.
- Write the answer to the riddle on the line below.

_____

Word Games • 2–3 © 2005 Creative Teaching Press

Synonyms and Antonyms

Vocabulary

Synonyms are words that mean the same thing.
(<u>happy</u> is to <u>glad</u> as <u>help</u> is to <u>aid</u>)
Antonyms are words that have opposite meanings.
(<u>up</u> is to <u>down</u> as <u>hot</u> is to <u>cold</u>)

Circle the letter next to the word that *best* completes each analogy.

1 <u>tardy</u> is to <u>late</u> as <u>nice</u> is to
- **a.** niece
- **b.** kind
- **c.** mean
- **d.** pretty

2 <u>on</u> is to <u>off</u> as <u>right</u> is to
- **a.** write
- **b.** correct
- **c.** wrong
- **d.** rigid

3 <u>straight</u> is to <u>crooked</u> as <u>fast</u> is to
- **a.** speedy
- **b.** quick
- **c.** fist
- **d.** slow

4 <u>sick</u> is to <u>ill</u> as <u>near</u> is to
- **a.** close
- **b.** far
- **c.** hear
- **d.** never

5 <u>vacant</u> is to <u>empty</u> as <u>shake</u> is to
- **a.** difficult
- **b.** shiver
- **c.** easy
- **d.** hard

6 <u>young</u> is to <u>old</u> as <u>plain</u> is to
- **a.** plane
- **b.** common
- **c.** simple
- **d.** fancy

7 <u>closed</u> is to <u>open</u> as <u>weak</u> is to
- **a.** strong
- **b.** tired
- **c.** week
- **d.** sick

8 <u>repair</u> is to <u>fix</u> as <u>huge</u> is to
- **a.** tiny
- **b.** small
- **c.** large
- **d.** hug

Rhyming Words and Homophones

Vocabulary

> **Rhyming words** have the same ending sounds but different
> beginning sounds. (hair and care)
> **Homophones** are words that sound the same but are spelled differently
> and mean different things. (blue and blew)

Circle the letter next to the word that *best* completes each analogy.

1 so is to sew as ant is to
- **a.** insect
- **b.** mammal
- **c.** uncle
- **d.** aunt

2 bright is to night as cat is to
- **a.** dog
- **b.** kitten
- **c.** mat
- **d.** whisker

3 sea is to see as road is to
- **a.** highway
- **b.** rode
- **c.** car
- **d.** street

4 mouse is to house as bed is to
- **a.** red
- **b.** sleep
- **c.** couch
- **d.** bid

5 choose is to chews as bear is to
- **a.** fur
- **b.** sleep
- **c.** den
- **d.** bare

6 hair is to care as pen is to
- **a.** pencil
- **b.** ink
- **c.** write
- **d.** hen

7 maid is to made as mail is to
- **a.** male
- **b.** letter
- **c.** envelope
- **d.** stamp

8 flower is to flour as whole is to
- **a.** entire
- **b.** hole
- **c.** many
- **d.** dig

Word Games • 2–3 © 2005 Creative Teaching Press

Name _____ Date _____

Groupings and Parts of a Whole

Vocabulary

An **analogy** is the relationship between one pair of words that serves as the basis for the creation of another pair of words. Circle the letter next to the word that *best* completes each analogy.

1 key is to piano as string is to
- **a.** violin
- **b.** rope
- **c.** twine
- **d.** music

2 tuna is to fish as moth is to
- **a.** butterfly
- **b.** reptile
- **c.** mammal
- **d.** insect

3 toe is to foot as finger is to
- **a.** head
- **b.** hand
- **c.** nail
- **d.** ring

4 singer is to choir as student is to
- **a.** pupil
- **b.** teacher
- **c.** class
- **d.** desk

5 elbow is to arm as knee is to
- **a.** see
- **b.** bone
- **c.** cap
- **d.** leg

6 lens is to camera as wheel is to
- **a.** round
- **b.** bicycle
- **c.** deal
- **d.** horn

7 robin is to bird as tulip is to
- **a.** rows
- **b.** smell
- **c.** flower
- **d.** thorn

8 player is to team as actor is to
- **a.** stage
- **b.** actress
- **c.** movie
- **d.** cast

Word Games • 2–3 © 2005 Creative Teaching Press

Characteristics

Vocabulary

An **analogy** is the relationship between one pair of words that serves as the basis for the creation of another pair of words. Circle the letter next to the word that *best* completes each analogy.

1 brick is to hard as cotton is to
   a. bandage
   b. soft
   c. wool
   d. gotten

2 ice is to cold as sun is to
   a. hot
   b. sky
   c. planet
   d. son

3 lemon is to sour as sugar is to
   a. salt
   b. coffee
   c. cream
   d. sweet

4 spot is to leopard as stripe is to
   a. main
   b. tiger
   c. hair
   d. monkey

5 trunk is to elephant as wing is to
   a. feather
   b. ring
   c. bird
   d. leg

6 whisper is to quiet as horn is to
   a. car
   b. loud
   c. born
   d. animal

7 gill is to fish as lung is to
   a. breath
   b. rung
   c. heart
   d. human

8 small is to wasp as huge is to
   a. enormous
   b. tiny
   c. dinosaur
   d. big

Word Games • 2–3 © 2005 Creative Teaching Press

Name _____ Date _____

Community Helpers

Vocabulary

An **analogy** is the relationship between one pair of words that serves as the basis for the creation of another pair of words. Circle the letter next to the word that *best* completes each analogy.

1 veterinarian is to animals as dentist is to
    a. teeth
    b. feet
    c. doctor
    d. office

2 nurse is to medicine as banker is to
    a. purse
    b. money
    c. vault
    d. tanker

3 judge is to court as teacher is to
    a. preacher
    b. instructor
    c. classroom
    d. pencil

4 flower is to florist as nail is to
    a. finger
    b. carpenter
    c. pail
    d. hammer

5 baton is to conductor as brush is to
    a. artist
    b. hair
    c. rush
    d. comb

6 spoon is to chef as whistle is to
    a. coach
    b. noise
    c. thistle
    d. nurse

7 janitor is to broom as plumber is to
    a. dumber
    b. whistle
    c. electrician
    d. wrench

8 airplane is to pilot as bus is to
    a. driver
    b. fuss
    c. automobile
    d. school

Insects and Mammals

Vocabulary

An **analogy** is the relationship between one pair of words that serves as the basis for the creation of another pair of words. Circle the letter next to the word that *best* completes each analogy.

1 beetle is to needle as roach is to
- **a.** coach
- **b.** bug
- **c.** insect
- **d.** termite

2 caterpillar is to crawl as flea is to
- **a.** bug
- **b.** plea
- **c.** dog
- **d.** jump

3 cub is to lion as kitten is to
- **a.** dog
- **b.** whiskers
- **c.** cat
- **d.** mammal

4 monkey is to monkeys as mouse is to
- **a.** louse
- **b.** mice
- **c.** mouses
- **d.** meeses

5 ant is to aunt as bee is to
- **a.** hive
- **b.** buzz
- **c.** see
- **d.** be

6 feelers is to antennae as answer is to
- **a.** reply
- **b.** dancer
- **c.** test
- **d.** question

7 bee is to be as deer is to
- **a.** antler
- **b.** dear
- **c.** fear
- **d.** doe

8 bat is to cave as whale is to
- **a.** dolphin
- **b.** wail
- **c.** ocean
- **d.** fish

Word Games • 2–3 © 2005 Creative Teaching Press

Name _____ Date _____

Geography
Vocabulary

An **analogy** is the relationship between one pair of words that serves as the basis for the creation of another pair of words. Circle the letter next to the word that *best* completes each analogy.

1 arctic is to cold as desert is to
    a. sand
    b. camel
    c. dessert
    d. hot

2 river is to liver as lake is to
    a. bake
    b. water
    c. ocean
    d. swim

3 Chicago is to city as Ohio is to
    a. island
    b. state
    c. country
    d. continent

4 plain is to plane as strait is to
    a. crooked
    b. narrow
    c. straight
    d. gate

5 east is to west as north is to
    a. forth
    b. direction
    c. compass
    d. south

6 land is to grand as hill is to
    a. mesa
    b. mountain
    c. fill
    d. mound

7 peak is to peek as scene is to
    a. seen
    b. play
    c. stage
    d. bean

8 globe is to round as map is to
    a. picture
    b. cap
    c. wall
    d. flat

Transportation and Communication

Vocabulary

An **analogy** is the relationship between one pair of words that serves as the basis for the creation of another pair of words. Circle the letter next to the word that *best* completes each analogy.

1. jet is to sky as canoe is to
   a. river
   b. boat
   c. paddle
   d. ship

2. ear is to listen as eye is to
   a. I
   b. see
   c. lid
   d. face

3. arrive is to leave as stale is to
   a. bread
   b. stall
   c. fresh
   d. old

4. wing is to airplane as wheel is to
   a. rubber
   b. round
   c. ambulance
   d. barge

5. boat is to goat as wagon is to
   a. wheel
   b. pioneer
   c. taxi
   d. dragon

6. mail is to male as hear is to
   a. fear
   b. here
   c. there
   d. sound

7. road is to truck as track is to
   a. train
   b. print
   c. back
   d. crossing

8. bus is to buses as journey is to
   a. journies
   b. car
   c. trip
   d. journeys

Word Games • 2–3 © 2005 Creative Teaching Press

Analogy Review #1

Vocabulary

Circle the letter next to the word that *best* completes each analogy.

1 boot is to shoe as cap is to
  a. shirt
  b. hair
  c. blouse
  d. hat

2 roar is to lion as meow is to
  a. cat
  b. dog
  c. sound
  d. lizard

3 needle is to thread as stamp is to
  a. lick
  b. envelope
  c. ramp
  d. stomp

4 girl is to woman as boy is to
  a. toy
  b. child
  c. man
  d. lad

5 dime is to ten as nickel is to
  a. dollar
  b. penny
  c. pickle
  d. five

6 eight is to ate as four is to
  a. for
  b. door
  c. quarter
  d. more

7 stick is to hockey as club is to
  a. baseball
  b. bat
  c. golf
  d. basketball

8 coat is to jacket as home is to
  a. roam
  b. house
  c. office
  d. cave

Analogy Review #2

Vocabulary

Circle the letter next to the word that *best* completes each analogy.

1 referee is to football as umpire is to
   a. baseball
   b. team
   c. boxing
   d. sport

2 money is to bank as book is to
   a. magazine
   b. library
   c. read
   d. page

3 seaweed is to ocean as cactus is to
   a. plant
   b. green
   c. thorns
   d. desert

4 sharp is to dull as inside is to
   a. outside
   b. house
   c. opposite
   d. shelter

5 monkey is to mammal as salmon is to
   a. ocean
   b. tuna
   c. fish
   d. plant

6 tomato is to tomatoes as shelf is to
   a. shelfs
   b. shelves
   c. kitchen
   d. counter

7 lettuce is to green as carrot is to
   a. fruit
   b. vegetable
   c. parrot
   d. orange

8 tent is to camper as ship is to
   a. trip
   b. ocean
   c. sailor
   d. land

Word Games • 2–3 © 2005 Creative Teaching Press

Analogy Review #3

Vocabulary

Circle the letter next to the word that *best* completes each analogy.

1 foot is to inches as yard is to
   a. grass
   b. hard
   c. mow
   d. feet

2 April is to month as Friday is to
   a. year
   b. Wednesday
   c. day
   d. minute

3 win is to lose as first is to
   a. last
   b. many
   c. burst
   d. quick

4 winter is to coat as summer is to
   a. warm
   b. season
   c. spring
   d. shorts

5 scramble is to egg as toss is to
   a. boss
   b. salad
   c. mix
   d. tosses

6 crayon is to draw as brush is to
   a. chalk
   b. rush
   c. paint
   d. bush

7 study is to studies as hero is to
   a. heroes
   b. heros
   c. leader
   d. zero

8 knight is to night as groan is to
   a. grown
   b. height
   c. moan
   d. tall

Word Games • 2–3 © 2005 Creative Teaching Press

Name _____ Date _____

Analogy Review #4

Vocabulary

Circle the letter next to the word that *best* completes each analogy.

1 <u>maple</u> is to <u>tree</u> as <u>pineapple</u> is to
  a. apple
  b. fish
  c. fruit
  d. vegetable

2 <u>smell</u> is to <u>odor</u> as <u>elect</u> is to
  a. president
  b. choose
  c. reject
  d. wine

3 <u>zebra</u> is to <u>mammal</u> as <u>cardinal</u> is to
  a. red
  b. insect
  c. bird
  d. zoo

4 <u>solve</u> is to <u>problem</u> as <u>answer</u> is to
  a. question
  b. reply
  c. ask
  d. talk

5 <u>trio</u> is to <u>three</u> as <u>pair</u> is to
  a. hair
  b. pear
  c. two
  d. five

6 <u>air</u> is to <u>gas</u> as <u>water</u> is to
  a. ocean
  b. liquid
  c. milk
  d. faucet

7 <u>fawn</u> is to <u>deer</u> as <u>kid</u> is to
  a. rid
  b. moose
  c. whale
  d. goat

8 <u>scissors</u> is to <u>cut</u> as <u>ax</u> is to
  a. chop
  b. tax
  c. tree
  d. blend

Word Games • 2–3 © 2005 Creative Teaching Press

Three-Letter Opposites

Antonyms, Vocabulary, and Spelling

For each word write a three-letter word that means its opposite in the boxes. The first one has been done for you.

1 dry | w | e | t

2 begin

3 cold

4 night

5 near

6 lose

7 on

8 bottom

9 happy

10 girl

11 high

12 in

Name _____ Date _____

Four-Letter Opposites

Antonyms, Vocabulary, and Spelling

For each word write a four-letter word that means its opposite in the boxes. The first one has been done for you.

1 front | b | a | c | k |

7 poor | | | | |

2 light | | | | |

8 start | | | | |

3 up | | | | |

9 pull | | | | |

4 early | | | | |

10 short | | | | |

5 easy | | | | |

11 false | | | | |

6 give | | | | |

12 narrow | | | | |

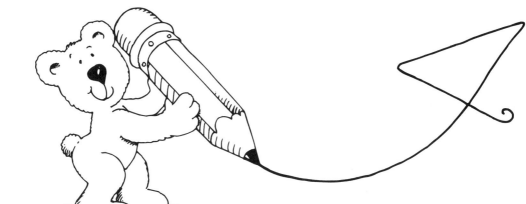

Five-Letter Opposites

Antonyms, Vocabulary, and Spelling

For each word write a five-letter word that means its opposite in the boxes. The first one has been done for you.

1 above | b | e | l | o | w |

7 asleep [ ][ ][ ][ ][ ]

2 always [ ][ ][ ][ ][ ]

8 plain [ ][ ][ ][ ][ ]

3 before [ ][ ][ ][ ][ ]

9 flimsy [ ][ ][ ][ ][ ]

4 clean [ ][ ][ ][ ][ ]

10 stale [ ][ ][ ][ ][ ]

5 large [ ][ ][ ][ ][ ]

11 seldom [ ][ ][ ][ ][ ]

6 heavy [ ][ ][ ][ ][ ]

12 smooth [ ][ ][ ][ ][ ]

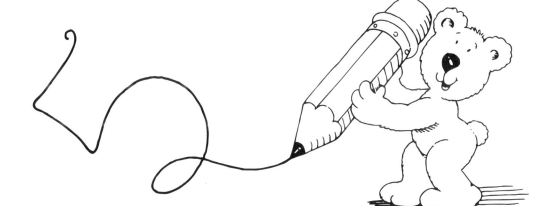

Odd Word Out

Classifying and Vocabulary

In each row find the word that does not belong. Circle the word and explain why it does not belong with the other words. Use a dictionary if you need help.

1 tiger   bird   dog   bear

_____

2 stove   bake   broil   fry

_____

3 eyes   nose   hand   ears

_____

4 red   blue   brown   crayon

_____

5 to   three   six   twelve

_____

6 day   week   month   mouth

_____

7 robin   salmon   canary   crow

_____

8 globe   ball   sun   box

_____

Word Games • 2–3 © 2005 Creative Teaching Press

More Odd Word Out

Classifying and Vocabulary

In each row find the word that does not belong. Circle the word and explain why it does not belong with the other words. Use a dictionary if you need help.

1 zebra   cobra   boa   python

_____

2 uncle   niece   father   nephew

_____

3 umbrella   rain   snow   wind

_____

4 oak   elm   pine   rose

_____

5 lamb   cat   puppy   calf

_____

6 sun   banana   lemon   blood

_____

7 milk   juice   steak   tea

_____

8 circle   square   triangle   paper

_____

Missing Mammal Vowels

Spelling

In each row fill in the missing vowels to spell the name of a mammal. Write the name of the mammal on the line. The first one has been done for you.

1 b _a_ t   bat

2 l ___ ___ n   _____

3 b ___ ___ r   _____

4 h ___ r s ___   _____

5 l l ___ m ___   _____

6 m ___ ___ s ___   _____

7 b ___ ___ v ___ r   _____

8 z ___ b r ___   _____

9 g ___ r ___ l l ___   _____

10 l ___ ___ p ___ r d   _____

11 j ___ c k ___ l   _____

12 r ___ c c ___ ___ n   _____

Word Games • 2–3 © 2005 Creative Teaching Press

More Missing Mammal Vowels

Spelling

In each row fill in the missing vowels to spell the name of a mammal. Write the name of the mammal on the line. The first one has been done for you.

1 w __o__ l f   _____wolf_____

2 c ____ m ____ l   _____

3 d ____ ____ r   _____

4 t ____ g ____ r   _____

5 g ____ r ____ f f ____   _____

6 w ____ l r ____ s   _____

7 k ____ ____ l ____   _____

8 b ____ d g ____ r   _____

9 w h ____ l ____   _____

10 s q ____ ____ r r ____ l   _____

11 h ____ m s t ____ r   _____

12 j ____ g ____ ____ r   _____

Compound Match-Ups

Compound Words and Spelling

A **compound word** is made up of two smaller words such as *in* + *side* = *inside*.

The compound words below are all mixed-up. Match each word in Column A with a word from Column B to make a compound word. Write the compound word on the line. Mark the box as you use each word. The first one has been done for you.

Column A		Column B
1 air	port_____	☐ light
2 in	_____	☐ ever
3 eye	_____	☐ boat
4 birth	_____	☐ paper
5 head	_____	☐ day
6 arm	_____	☒ port
7 how	_____	☐ chair
8 blue	_____	☐ lash
9 life	_____	☐ stick
10 water	_____	☐ side
11 yard	_____	☐ bird
12 wall	_____	☐ melon

Word Games • 2–3 © 2005 Creative Teaching Press

More Compound Match-Ups

Compound Words and Spelling

A **compound word** is made up of two smaller words such as *out + side = outside.*

The compound words below are all mixed-up. Match each word in Column A with a word from Column B to make a compound word. Write the compound word on the line. Mark the box as you use each word. The first one has been done for you.

Column A

1 pine   apple _____

2 sea   _____

3 wind   _____

4 what   _____

5 sky   _____

6 neck   _____

7 mail   _____

8 jelly   _____

9 rail   _____

10 pop   _____

11 lady   _____

12 pan   _____

Column B

☐ mill

☐ tie

☐ fish

☐ shore

☐ corn

☐ cake

☐ line

☐ bug

☒ apple

☐ box

☐ road

☐ ever

Name _____ Date _____

Lots of Bubbles

Spelling and Vocabulary

How many words can you find in the bubbles? Write the words you find on the lines below. Use the back of your paper if you need more room. *(Hint: There are more than **20** words!)*

Rules

- The words you find must have three or more letters.
- Start on any bubble and move to an adjacent bubble connected by a line to the left, right, or in the middle. You may not skip a bubble.
  Examples: **BAT** is allowed because each bubble is next to the other and is connected by a line.
  BAY is not allowed because the letters **A** and **Y** are not next to each other and their bubbles are not connected by a line.
- You may not use the same letter twice in a row, but you can go back and use a letter again in the same word.
  Example: **WOW** is allowed, but **BORROW** is not.

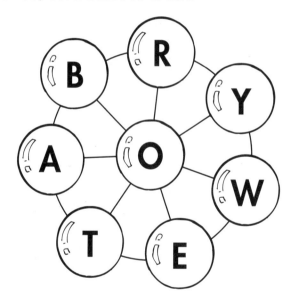

Words I Found

_____ _____ _____

_____ _____ _____

_____ _____ _____

_____ _____ _____

_____ _____ _____

Name _____ Date _____

In the Garden

Spelling and Vocabulary

How many words can you find in the flower? Write the words you find on the lines below. Use the back of your paper if you need more room. *(Hint: There are more than 20 words!)*

Rules
- The words you find must have three or more letters.
- Start in the center of the flower or on any petal and move from petal to petal or to the center to spell a word. You may not skip a petal.

  Examples: **RAID** is allowed because each petal is touching another petal or the letter in the center.

  MADE is not allowed because the petals with the letters **D** and **E** are not touching each other.

- You may not use the same letter twice in a row, but you can go back and use a letter again in the same word.

  Example: **DAD** is allowed, but **DADDY** is not.

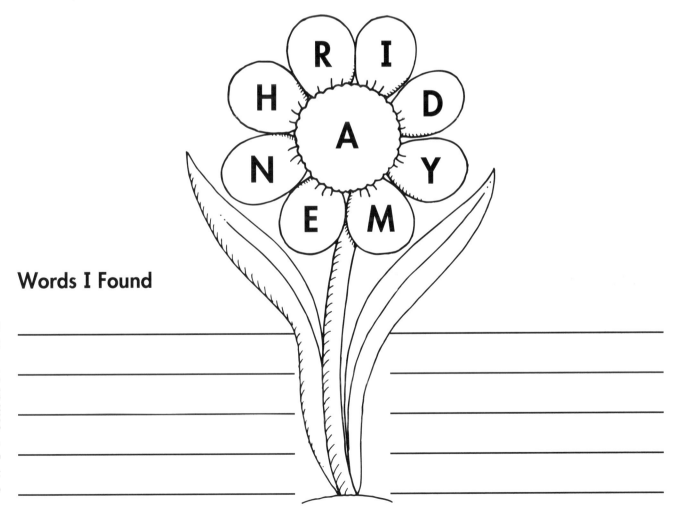

Words I Found

_____ _____

_____ _____

_____ _____

_____ _____

Pizza Puzzle

Spelling and Vocabulary

How many words can you find in the pizza? Write the words you find on the lines below. Use the back of your paper if you need more room. *(Hint: There are more than **40** words!)*

Rules

- The words you find must have three or more letters.
- Start on any letter in the pizza and move to any circle connected by a line to spell a word. You may not skip a circle.
  Examples: **TEA** is allowed because each circle is connected by a line.
  DATE is not allowed because the letter **D** is not connected to the letter **A**.
- You may not use the same letter twice in a row, but you can go back and use a letter again in the same word.
  Example: **TESTS** is allowed, but **MESS** is not.
- Plurals are allowed.
  Example: **MATS**

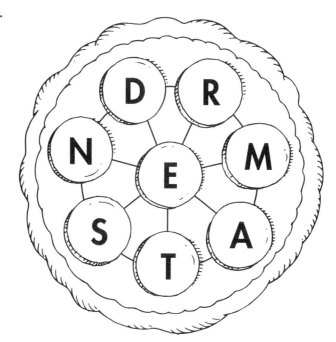

Words I Found

_____ _____ _____

_____ _____ _____

_____ _____ _____

_____ _____ _____

_____ _____ _____

Word Games • 2–3 © 2005 Creative Teaching Press

Name _____   Date _____

Magic Word Square #1

Spelling and Vocabulary

How many words can you find in the square? Write the words you find on the lines. Use the back of the paper if you need more space. *(Hint: There are more than 55 words!)*

Rules

- The words you find must have three or more letters.
- Start on any square and move one square in any direction. You may not skip a square when making your word.
- Plurals are allowed.
- You may not use a letter twice in a row.

M	I	A	B
H	U	T	O
N	E	S	P
L	R	V	Y

Words I Found

_____   _____   _____

_____   _____   _____

_____   _____   _____

_____   _____   _____

_____   _____   _____

_____   _____   _____

_____   _____   _____

_____   _____   _____

Word Games • 2–3 © 2005 Creative Teaching Press

Magic Word Square #2

Spelling and Vocabulary

How many words can you find in the square? Write the words you find on the lines. Use the back of the paper if you need more space. *(Hint: There are more than **80** words!)*

Rules

- The words you find must have three or more letters.
- Start on any square and move one square in any direction. You may not skip a square when making your word.
- Plurals are allowed.
- You may not use a letter twice in a row.

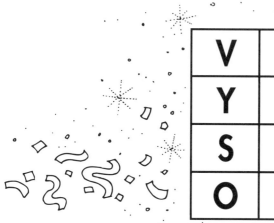

V	I	C	U
Y	W	E	D
S	T	A	P
O	R	M	F

Words I Found

_____ _____ _____

_____ _____ _____

_____ _____ _____

_____ _____ _____

_____ _____ _____

_____ _____ _____

_____ _____ _____

_____ _____ _____

Word Games • 2–3 © 2005 Creative Teaching Press

Answer Key

Consonant Blend Clown (page 5)

words with *dr* blend: drift, drag

word with *tr* blend: trail

words with *wh* blend: whale, wharf, when, which, whine, whiz

words with *bl* blend: blast, blanket

word with *cr* blend: crate

word with *cl* blend: climb

Phonics Fish (page 6)

words with *st* blend: stair, staff, stamp, stall, stale, star

words with *sn* blend: snob, snap, snug

words with *gr* blend: grape, grade

word with *sk* blend: skirt

words with *fr* blend: fresh, from

words with *br* blend: brawl, broil

Consonant Digraph Flower (page 7)

words with *kn* digraph: knit, knack, knead, knight, knife

words with *ch* digraph: chop, chill, cheer

words with *ph* digraph: phone, photo

word with *wr* digraph: wrestle

words with *th* digraph: thank, them, the, this

Bubble Gum Digraphs (page 8)

words with *ch* digraph: bench, beach, lunch, bunch, inch, lurch

words with *ck* digraph: black, deck, quick

words with *ng* digraph: hung, rung

words with *th* digraph: booth, tooth

Who's Wise? (page 9)

words with the sound of soft *c*: center, cylinder, cement, celebrate, certain, cereal, city, cent

words with the sound of hard *c*: car, comb, candle, cap, carrot, cold, crow

Going for Gold (page 10)

words with the sound of soft *g*: gentle, giant, giraffe, gym, germ, gesture

words with the sound of hard *g*: glow, guard, guess, gab, grand, grip, gulf, game, garden

Syllable Seal (page 11)

1-syllable words: through, straight

2-syllable words: letter, silly, freedom

3-syllable words: successful, example, principal

4-syllable words: automobile, investigate

5-syllable word: imagination

6-syllable word: encyclopedia

Double Scoops (page 12)

words with *bb*: rabbit, rubbish, cabbage

words with *dd*: middle, muddy

words with *ff*: fluffy, coffee

words with *ll*: galley, silly, hilly

words with *rr*: error, sorry, terror

words with *tt*: bottle, hitting, little

Rhyming Word Robot (page 13)

The robot should be colored as follows:

red—rake, make, lake

yellow—greet, wheat, meat, feet

green—sing, wing

brown—test, rest, guest, nest

orange—light, fight

blue—plot, got

purple—play, tray, say

black—fit, quit

Colorful Words (page 14)

1. fan
2. had
3. van
4. mat
5. sat
6. cap
7. tag
8. back
9. camp
10. sand
11. tack
12. plan

Alphabet Soup (page 17)

1. hop
2. mop
3. fog
4. box
5. hot
6. lot
7. pop
8. job
9. fox
10. mom
11. rock
12. sock

Scrambled Eggs (page 15)

1. wet
2. fed
3. jet
4. men
5. beg
6. web
7. best
8. bell
9. desk
10. rest
11. west
12. kept

The Jelly Bean Jar (page 18)

1. cub
2. fun
3. rug
4. hug
5. pup
6. rub
7. cup
8. dug
9. must
10. bump
11. duck
12. bug

What's the Scoop? (page 16)

1. fix
2. bit
3. big
4. did
5. him
6. wig
7. win
8. fill
9. pin (or nip)
10. milk
11. pick
12. hint (or thin)

Hooray for Long A (page 19)

1. cake
2. cane
3. lake
4. face
5. rake
6. cave
7. rain
8. snake
9. eight
10. frame

Long E, Please (page 20)

1. bee
2. key
3. tea
4. leaf
5. beet
6. seat
7. feet
8. tree
9. meat
10. wheat

Cute Long U (page 23)

1. use
2. blue
3. cube
4. huge
5. unit
6. tune
7. rude
8. tube
9. bugle
10. flute

I Like Long I (page 21)

1. pie
2. mice
3. dime
4. bike
5. five
6. kite
7. nine
8. time
9. night
10. smile

Word Scramble (page 24)

1. crib
2. sled
3. crab
4. plane
5. clock
6. plate
7. fruit
8. skunk
9. spoon
10. whale

I Know Long O (page 22)

1. toe
2. road
3. rose
4. hose
5. bone
6. soap
7. cone
8. nose
9. goat
10. globe

Bird Search (page 25)

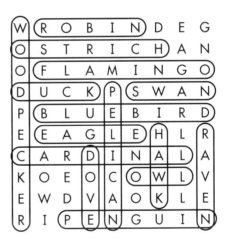

Color Search (page 26)

Fruit Search (page 29)

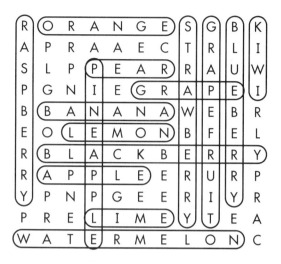

Mammal Search (page 27)

Vegetable Search (page 30)

Flower Search (page 28)

Weather Search (page 31)

```
M S D R I Z Z L E
I R F R O S T I E
S N O W N F O G U
T H U N D E R H R
I C I C L E N T C
H U R R I C A N E
A Z C L O U D I L
I R A I N O O N A
L W I N D E W G L
```

City Search (page 32)

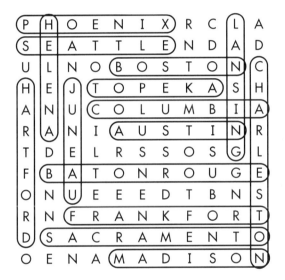

```
P H O E N I X R C L A
S E A T T L E N D A D
U L N O B O S T O N C H
H E J T O P E K A S H
A N U C O L U M B I A R
R A N I A U S T I N G L
T D E L R S S O S G E
F O B A T O N R O U G E
O N U E E E D T B N S
R N F R A N K F O R T
D S A C R A M E N T O
O E N A M A D I S O N
```

Community Helper Search (page 33)

```
P T A B A N K E R C P A
O R U L L B R O A F
L U T U J L A K R K L R
I C E S D I B K D A U F
C K A D R U B E V D E M C
E D H I G A R D E N E R
O R E V E R E D N T R C
F I R E F I G H T E R O
F V F R I A R I I R N A
I E E R F N F B S E E C
C R R A R D O C T O R H
E V C F R R R J E L R F
R A R I E A T R R G I A
```

State Search (page 34)

```
M A R Y L A N D S T
I P T S M O N I R E
S U E S S O H H I T X
S I N S M O A W O A A
I I A N T I W R E S
S D E L A W A R E S
S A L A A A I M O E
S H S S A W N O W
I O E K P A A N I
P A E A D R U T A H
I W I S C O N S I N
```

Tolerance Search (page 35)

```
R U N R E O U N H C I T I
E N E I G F I N O N M D E
S D T C S O G T N H R K I
P E C O U R A G E E E I G
O R O N N G C S S L S N O
N S M A A I O P T P E D A
S T P T G V M A Y I P N A
I A A C C E P T A N C E S
B N S A D N R I A G T S H
I D S R A E O E R C G S A
L I I A C M N N A I O R
I N O N C S M I C L N K E I
T G N G H R S E R I P I N
Y T E T O L E R A N C E G
```

Transportation Search (page 36)

```
M S A T A X I C A B
O K M R S A A R E L
T A B O T R U C K I
O T U L R B T E E M
R E L L B U O M O P
C B A E R E N B I C
Y O N C S C M O B A
C A C E T A N B N
L R E B E A I O I O
E D A I R P L A N E
B I C Y C L E T M O
```

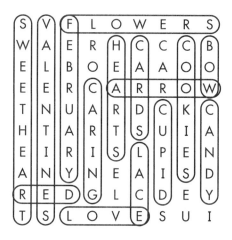

Valentine's Day Search (page 37)

```
S V F L O W E R S
W A E R O H C C C B
E L E O E A A O O
E E R C A R R O W
T N U A R D C K N
H T A R I S C U I D
E I R N E A P I D
A N Y G L A C D E
R E D G L C D U Y
T S L O V E S U I
```

Thanksgiving Search (page 38)

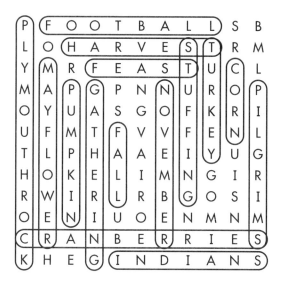

```
P F O O T B A L L S B
L O H A R V E S T R M
Y M R F E A S T U R L
M A P G P N N U C P
O Y U A S G O F O I
U F M T F V A F R L
T L P K A L I M N N G
H O K I L A R I U R
R W E N I U O E S I
O E N I B E N M M
C R A N B E R R I E S
K H E G I N D I A N S
```

Hanukkah Search (page 39)

```
G  T E M P L E  A R  S
O I L I G H T S  S  O
D A C R H M K F  P  N
L F R A H E N T  R  G
C E A C A N D L E  S
G S S L N O R L S  E
E T A E U R E A E  I
L I M N K R I T N  G
T V L T K H D K T  H
M A C C A B E E S  T
M L R R H L L S E  M
```

Christmas Search (page 40)

```
E L F C S G I A C Y
S S T O C K I N G S
D E C E M B E R M A
T C A R O L S E I N
O R N A M E N T S T
Y D D A N G E L T A
S S L E I G H R L C
W R E A T H L Y E L
T I S H O L L Y T A
R E I N D E E R O U
C A N D Y C A N E S
```

Short Vowel Words (page 41)

Answers will vary. Possible answers include:
Short a—bat, ham, pan, tan, mat
Short e—bell, hen, pen, tent, men
Short i—bin, hit, pill, tin, mitt
Short o—box, hog, pot, top, mop
Short u—bus, hunt, putt, tusk, mud

Long Vowel Words (page 42)

Answers will vary. Possible answers include:
Long a—bake, fake, make, rain, say
Long e—beet, feed, meat, reef, see
Long i—bite, fight, might, right, sign
Long o—bone, foam, mole, road, soap
Long u—blue, fuse, mule, ruin, suit

Fun with Words (page 43)

Answers will vary. Possible answers include:
One-Syllable Word—ant, mint, no, oak, won
Two-Syllable Word—apple, monkey, needle, order, winner
Plural Word—ants, mules, noses, owls, wheels
Compound Word—airplane, motorboat, notebook,
   oatmeal, watermelon
Noun—animal, menu, nest, octopus, wagon

Colors (page 44)

Answers will vary. Possible answers include:
Red—barn, gem, dynamite, lipstick, fire engine
Yellow—buttercup, galoshes, daffodil, lemon,
   frozen banana
Blue—blueberry, garment, dress, larkspur, fins
Green—bean, grass, dinosaur, leaf, fern
Brown—bear, gopher, dirt, leather, fawn

Around the House (page 45)

Answers will vary. Possible answers include:
In the Kitchen—toaster, cups, blender, stove, refrigerator
In the Living Room—table, couch, blinds, stereo, rug
In the Bathroom—tub, cabinet, brush, soap, rollers
In the Bedroom—toys, clothes, bed, sheet, radio
In the Family Room—television, carpet, books, sofa,
   remote control

Plants and Animals (page 46)

Answers will vary. Possible answers include:
Mammal—bear, tiger, dog, pig, goat
Bird—blue jay, toucan, duck, parrot, goose
Fish—barracuda, tuna, damsel, piranha, goldfish
Flower—begonia, tulip, daisy, petunia, gardenia
Tree—birch, tulip tree, dogwood, pine, gum

People (page 47)

Answers will vary. Possible answers include:
Boy's Name—Albert, Frank, Lance, Nick, Charles
Girl's Name—Ashley, Francine, Lisa, Nancy, Carrie
Famous Person—Armstrong, Franklin, Lincoln,
    Nicklaus, Columbus
Community Helper—artist, firefighter, librarian,
    nurse, chef
Actor or Actress—Affleck, Ford, Lopez, Nicholson,
    Carrey

Leisure Time (page 48)

Answers will vary. Possible answers include:
Television Show—Rugrats, George Shrinks, Blue's Clues,
    Out of the Box, Power Rangers
Sport or Game—rugby, golf, baseball, Old Maid, polo
Book—Rapunzel, Grandfather's Journey, Babar the King,
    Ox-Cart Man, Polar Express
Song—Row, Row, Row Your Boat, Green Grass Grows
    All Around, B-I-N-G-O, Old MacDonald Had a Farm,
    Pop! Goes the Weasel
Movie—Rescuers Down Under, George of the Jungle,
    Bambi, Old Yeller, Peter Pan

On the Menu (page 49)

Answers will vary. Possible answers include:
Fruit—mango, cantaloupe, pineapple, banana,
    strawberry
Vegetable—mushroom, carrot, pea, beet, sweet potato
Dessert—mousse, cake, pie, baked apple, sundae
Main Course—meatloaf, casserole, pizza, beef,
    spaghetti
Drink—milk, coffee, punch, berry juice, soda

Shopping Spree (page 50)

Answers will vary. Possible answers include:
Department Store—coffee maker, pants, shoes,
    T-shirt, dress
Furniture Store—cabinet, pillow, sofa, table, dresser
Office Supply Store—copier, paper, stapler, toner, desk
Toy Store—car, playhouse, skateboard, truck, doll
Grocery Store—cereal, pickles, soda, tea, donuts

Rhyming Crisscross (page 51)

Across	Down
1. bug	mug
2. fear	near
3. beak	week
4. spring	wing
5. nest	test
6. groom	broom
7. snake	rake
8. play	stay

More Rhyming Crisscross (page 52)

Across	Down
1. day	jay
2. twig	big
3. rink	stink
4. quack	sack
5. lamb	jam
6. blank	bank
7. small	ball
8. king	ring

Verb Tense Crisscross (page 53)

Across	Down
1. ran	ate
2. drank	forgot
3. froze	shook
4. wrote	wore
5. chose	spoke
6. threw	shrunk
7. rode	broke
8. went	flew

Synonym Crisscross (page 54)

Across	Down
1. real	rush
2. mend	near
3. strong	wet
4. occur	copy
5. wise	entire
6. zone	ache
7. shine	aid
8. rule	blend

Opposite Word Crisscross (page 55)

Across	Down
1. cold	soft
2. none	end
3. worst	top
4. clean	back
5. pretty	after
6. alike	few
7. high	quiet
8. thick	wild

Measurement Crossword Puzzle (page 56)

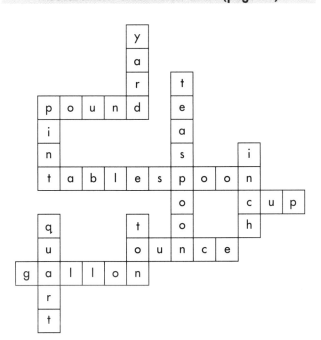

Zoo Crossword Puzzle (page 57)

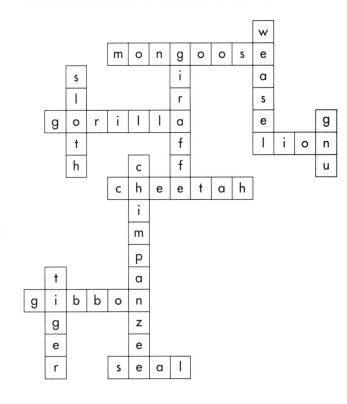

Collection Crossword Puzzle (page 58)

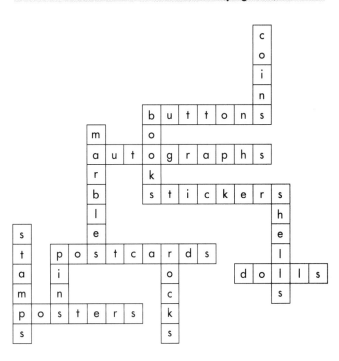

Things with Holes Crossword Puzzle (page 59)

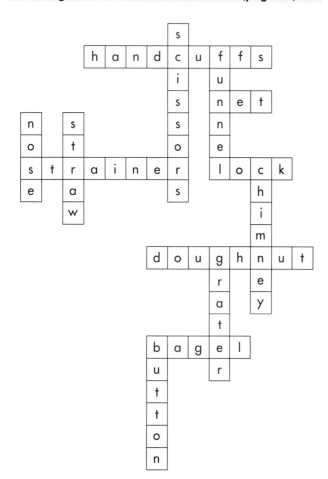

Noun Crossword Puzzle #2 (page 61)

Across
2. mate
4. blaze
6. valley
8. aorta
10. plan
12. edge

Down
1. kettle
3. lava
5. lizard
8. ankle

Verb Crossword Puzzle (page 62)

Across
2. warn
4. extend
6. relax
8. cause
10. give

Down
1. twinkle
3. unite
5. lend
7. select
9. urge

Adjective Crossword Puzzle (page 63)

Across
2. lively
4. imaginary
6. careful
8. cruel
10. temporary

Down
1. reliable
3. ignorant
5. hardy
7. flimsy
9. dual

Noun Crossword Puzzle #1 (page 60)

Across
2. hoof
4. rage
6. colt
8. opera
10. neighbor

Down
1. globe
3. forest
5. error
7. acorn
9. quarrel

Plurals Crossword Puzzle (page 64)

Across
3. foxes
5. babies
7. children
9. mice
11. calves
13. geese
15. halves
16. tomatoes

Down
1. women
2. donkeys
4. tools
6. bunnies
8. heroes
10. cargoes
12. altos
14. men

Eat It, Wear It, or Plant It? (page 65)

<u>Eat It</u>
custard
goulash
stew
tofu

<u>Wear It</u>
vest
cape
cardigan
scarf

<u>Plant It</u>
violet
daffodil
iris
marigold

Mammal, Fish, or Reptile? (page 67)

<u>Mammal</u>
otter
hyena
mole
yak

<u>Fish</u>
cod
stingray
trout
marlin

<u>Reptile</u>
alligator
turtle
snake
tortoise

Land, Sea, or Air Animal? (page 66)

<u>On Land</u>
beagle
cheetah
ocelot
camel

<u>In the Sea</u>
perch
bass
minnow
mackerel

<u>In the Air</u>
hawk
bee
raven
robin

Fruit, Vegetable, or Tree? (page 68)

<u>Fruit</u>
kiwi
strawberry
watermelon
grape

<u>Vegetable</u>
broccoli
cauliflower
asparagus
spinach

<u>Tree</u>
sequoia
cedar
spruce
magnolia

Noun, Verb, or Adjective? (page 69)

Noun
meat
crowd
lizard
joy

Verb
was
asked
spoke
ran

Adjective
fast
gloomy
frisky
great

Feet, Head, or Body? (page 70)

Worn on the Feet
slippers
cleats
sneakers
boots
sandals

Worn on the Head
sombrero
crown
bonnet
cap
helmet

Worn Somewhere Else on the Body
robe
cloak
tuxedo
jacket
suspenders

Travel by Land, Water, or Air? (page 71)

Travel by Land
tricycle
tractor
moped
scooter
bus

Travel by Water
raft
kayak
submarine
yacht
ferry

Travel by Air
helicopter
blimp
jet
rocket
hot air balloon

Hold, Measure, or Read? (page 72)

Items That Hold Things
bowl
basket
bucket
vase
hamper

Items That Are Used for Measuring
thermometer
clock
ruler
odometer
speedometer

Something That Is Read
almanac
catalog
encyclopedia
brochure
magazine

Play It, Sing It, or Dance It? (page 73)

A Musical Instrument
flute

harp

clarinet

tuba

oboe

Things You Can Sing
chorus

lullaby

opera

melody

tune

Kinds of Dances
ballet

tango

hula

polka

waltz

Football, Baseball, or Basketball? (page 74)

Football Terms
kickoff

huddle

punt

tackle

touchdown

Baseball Terms
bunt

pitch

walk

fly

diamond

Basketball Terms
rebound

hoop

jump shot

dribble

court

Riddle #1 (page 75)
I dig you

Riddle #2 (page 76)
corn on the cob

Riddle #3 (page 77)
one with no springs

Riddle #4 (page 78)
a comb

Riddle #5 (page 79)
they are always spotted

Riddle #6 (page 80)
she got the point

Riddle #7 (page 81)
a blackboard

Riddle #8 (page 82)
they brake dance

Riddle #9 (page 83)
flying saucers

Riddle #10 (page 84)

I do not peel very well

Synonyms and Antonyms (page 85)

1. b
2. c
3. d
4. a
5. b
6. d
7. a
8. c

Rhyming Words and Homophones (page 86)

1. d
2. c
3. b
4. a
5. d
6. d
7. a
8. b

Groupings and Parts of a Whole (page 87)

1. a
2. d
3. b
4. c
5. d
6. b
7. c
8. d

Characteristics (page 88)

1. b
2. a
3. d
4. b
5. c
6. b
7. d
8. c

Community Helpers (page 89)

1. a
2. b
3. c
4. b
5. a
6. a
7. d
8. a

Insects and Mammals (page 90)

1. a
2. d
3. c
4. b
5. d
6. a
7. b
8. c

Geography (page 91)

1. d
2. a
3. b
4. c
5. d
6. c
7. a
8. d

Transportation and Communication (page 92)

1. a
2. b
3. c
4. c
5. d
6. b
7. a
8. d

Analogy Review #1 (page 93)

1. d
2. a
3. b
4. c
5. d
6. a
7. c
8. b

Analogy Review #2 (page 94)

1. a
2. b
3. d
4. a
5. c
6. b
7. d
8. c

Analogy Review #3 (page 95)

1. d
2. c
3. a
4. d
5. b
6. c
7. a
8. a

Analogy Review #4 (page 96)

1. c
2. b
3. c
4. a
5. c
6. b
7. d
8. a

Three-Letter Opposites (page 97)

1. wet
2. end
3. hot
4. day
5. far
6. win
7. off
8. top
9. sad
10. boy
11. low
12. out

Four-Letter Opposites (page 98)

1. back
2. dark
3. down
4. late
5. hard
6. take
7. rich
8. stop
9. push
10. tall
11. true (or real)
12. wide

Five-Letter Opposites (page 99)

1. below
2. never
3. after
4. dirty
5. small
6. light
7. awake
8. fancy
9. solid
10. fresh
11. often
12. rough

Odd Word Out (page 100)

1. bird—not a mammal
2. stove—not a way to cook food
3. hand—not a part of the head or face
4. crayon—not the name of a color
5. to—not the name of a number
6. mouth—not a measurement of time
7. salmon—not the name of a bird
8. box—not an object that is round

More Odd Word Out (page 101)

1. zebra—not the name of a snake
2. niece—not a male relative
3. umbrella—not a type of weather
4. rose—not the name of a tree
5. cat—not the name of a baby animal
6. blood—not an object that is yellow
7. steak—not something you drink; not a liquid
8. paper—not the name of a geometric shape

Missing Mammal Vowels (page 102)

1. bat
2. lion
3. bear (or boar)
4. horse
5. llama
6. mouse (or moose)
7. beaver
8. zebra
9. gorilla
10. leopard
11. jackal
12. raccoon

More Missing Mammal Vowels (page 103)

1. wolf
2. camel
3. deer
4. tiger
5. giraffe
6. walrus
7. koala
8. badger
9. whale
10. squirrel
11. hamster
12. jaguar

Compound Match-Ups (page 104)

1. airport
2. inside
3. eyelash
4. birthday
5. headlight
6. armchair
7. however
8. bluebird
9. lifeboat
10. watermelon
11. yardstick
12. wallpaper

More Compound Match-Ups (page 105)

1. pineapple
2. seashore
3. windmill
4. whatever
5. skyline
6. necktie
7. mailbox
8. jellyfish
9. railroad
10. popcorn
11. ladybug
12. pancake

Lots of Bubbles (page 106)

Answers will vary. Possible answers include:

ate	roe
bat	rot
boat	rote
bow	row
boy	tab
brow	toe
ewe	tot
oat	tow
orb	toy
owe	wet
rob	woe
robot	wow

In the Garden (page 107)

Answers will vary. Possible answers include:

aha	mad
aid	man
arid	mar
dad	may
dam	name
dame	nay
did	near
ear	raid
had	ram
hah	ray
hair	yam
ham	

Pizza Puzzle (page 108)

Answers will vary. Possible answers include:

amend	nests
ate	ream
den	red
dens	render
dense	rest
denser	rests
detest	retest
detests	retests
eat	sea
eater	seam
eats	seat
end	seats
ended	send
mat	sender
mats	set
meat	sets
meats	steam
men	stem
mend	tender
neat	test
nest	tests

Answers will vary. Possible answers include:

aim	nests
atop	nut
auto	nuts
autos	post
bait	posts
baits	pot
bat	pots
bats	rest
boat	rests
boats	set
bop	sets
bops	sob
her	spy
hers	stab
hiatus	stop
him	stops
hit	sum
hits	sun
hum	tab
hut	tat
huts	tats
let	test
lets	tests
mite	top
mites	tops
must	tot
nerve	tots
nerves	tune
nest	tunes

Answers will vary. Possible answers include:

amp	paws
ape	pear
aped	pears
arm	peat
art	pep
arts	ram
ate	ramp
awe	rap
awed	rat
cud	rate
dad	rated
damp	rats
data	rot
date	rots
dew	sort
dews	sorts
dud	stamp
due	stamped
ear	star
ears	start
eat	steam
ewe	stew
farm	stewed
fat	stews
fate	storm
fated	sweat
fats	sweats
ice	tad
iced	tap
map	tape
mar	taped
mat	tea
mate	tear
mated	tears
pad	tot
part	tots
parts	wad
party	wade
pat	waded
pate	wed
pats	wet
paw	wets
pawed	